C000121076

Answer
Book

Introduction

Pupils' written work

Abacus Evolve textbooks provide clear guidance to pupils on how their work should be recorded. Pupils should be encouraged to follow this guidance, which will make marking their work substantially easier and clearly focused.

Marking pupils' work

Clearly it is important that pupils' work is seen and checked by the teacher regularly, but it is not necessary for all work to be marked by the teacher. Decisions about which work should be teacher-marked, and how it should be marked will be made alongside the need to maximise time available for teaching and guiding pupils through their activities.

A suggested approach within *Abacus Evolve* is to make these decisions Unit by Unit. Decide, for example, for each Unit, which parts you want to mark, and which parts the pupils can mark.

Marking the 'Owls'

The 'Owls' are optional problem-solving or investigational activities for extra challenge on each page. They should generally be marked by the teacher. The pupils' responses to the 'Owls' may well vary because of the often open-ended nature of the activities, however the answers give suggestions where appropriate. Pupils should also be encouraged to use a systematic approach to solving these problems, where relevant.

For many 'Owls' you may want to ask the pupils to work in groups or pairs, possibly leading to a group display of their results.

Contents

Block A1

page 3
Counting in 1s and 10s

1. 37, 38, 46, 47, 48, 57
2. 15, 24, 25, 26, 34, 35
3. 14, 23, 24, 34, 35
4. 77, 78, 79, 88, 98
5. 6, 16, 26, 27, 28
6. 68, 77, 78, 79, 88, 98, 99
7. 3, 13, 14, 15, 23, 25
8. 34, 35, 36, 44, 46, 54, 56
9. 217, 218, 219, 220
10. 314, 315, 316, 317
11. 568, 569, 570, 571
12. 849, 850, 851, 852
13. 917, 918, 919, 920
14. 108, 109, 110, 111
Owl Answers will vary.

page 4
Counting in 1s and 10s

1. 103, 104, 105
2. 550, 551, 552
3. 280, 281, 282
4. 400, 401, 402
5. 257, 258, 259
6. 198, 199, 200
7. £465, £463
8. £501, £499
9. £700, £698
10. £776, £774
11. £402, £400
12. £310, £308
13. £811, £809

Add £10 to each price:
7. £474
8. £510
9. £709

10. £785
11. £411
12. £319
13. £820
Owl 20, 20

page 5
Comparing numbers

1. (b) has most
2. (b) has most
3. (a) has most
4. (a) has most
5. £2·01
6. 51p
7. 7p
8. 91p
9. 2p
10. £6·01
11. £2·00
12. £2·50
13. £1·18
14. £3·70
Owl Five

page 6
Counting in 10s and 100s

1. 1000
2. Children will draw a 10 × 10 grid, starting at 10 in the first row and ending at 1000.
Owl 171
3. 4842, 4942
4. 5297, 5397
5. 7040, 7140
6. 3331, 3431
7. 999, 1099
8. 5679, 5779
9. 659, 759
10. 2211, 2311

page 7

Hundreds, tens and units

1. 40 + 7 = 47
2. 60 + 7 = 67
3. 90 + 1 = 91
4. 100 + 70 + 3 = 173
5. 300 + 60 + 3 = 363
6. 800 + 60 = 860
7. 900 + 2 = 902
8. 400 + 10 + 4 = 414
9. 200 + 10 + 2 = 212
10. 6 tens
11. 1 ten
12. 2 tens
13. 0 tens
14. 9 tens
15. 5 tens
Owl 11, 22, 33, 44, 55, 66, 77, 88, 99

page 8

Hundreds, tens and units

1. 361
2. 405
3. 682
4. 240
5. 110
6. 345

In size order: 110, 240, 345, 361, 405, 682
Owl 21
7. €347 + €100 = €447
8. €281 + €100 = €381
9. €607 + €100 = €707
10. €84 + €100 = €184
11. €840 + €100 = €940
12. €500 + €100 = €600
13. €916 + €100 = €1016

page 9

Hundreds, tens and units

1. €122
2. €516

3. €300
4. €125
5. €101
Owl Answers will vary. An example might be 306 + 194 = 500.
6. A number from 633 to 646
7. A number from 108 to 116
8. A number from 299 to 300
9. A number from 451 to 454
10. A number from 345 to 371
11. A number from 570 to 572

page 10

Hundreds, tens and units

1. Answers will vary. Possible answers include 343, 118, 613 or 253.
2. 113 or 133
   Children will draw a 10 × 8 grid, starting at 100 in the first row and ending at 8000.
3. 4500
4. 10 000
5. 6100
6. 3000
7. Answers will vary. The sum of the numbers in opposite corners will be the same.
Owl Answers will vary. An example might be a computer or a radio.

page 11

Counting

1. 13
2. 67

page 12

Counting

1. 54
2. red 20, blue 17, yellow 17, not red 34

page 12 continued

3.

15 marbles, 3 groups of 5

21 marbles, 4 groups of 5, plus 1

page 13

Counting: grouping in 5s and 10s

1. 27
2. 39
3. 18
4. 21
5. 43
6. 57
7. 42
8. 55
9. 60
10. 37
11. 45

page 14

I more, I less, 10 more, 10 less

1. 65
2. 21
3. 60
4. 36
5. 47
6. 31

With one shell taken out of each basket:

1. 63
2. 19
3. 58
4. 34
5. 45

6. 29
7. 54, 56, 65
8. 22, 33, 42
9. 67, 76, 78, 87
10. 66, 75
11. 48, 50, 58, 60
12. 27, 35, 46

Owl Answers will vary. Possible answers include 45, 34; 78, 67.

page 15

I more, I less, 10 more, 10 less

1. 148
2. 266
3. 340
4. 554
5. 128
6. 460

The page number before:

1. 145
2. 263
3. 337
4. 551
5. 125
6. 457

Owl 171

7. £178
8. £280
9. £374
10. £155
11. £470
12. £232

page 16

10 more, 10 less, 100 more, 100 less

1. (a) 430   (b) 550   (c) 580
   (d) 620   (e) 660   (f) 730
   (g) 790   (h) 850   (i) 860
   (j) 700   (k) 990   (l) 970
   (m) 820   (n) 690
   1000, 1010, 1020, 1030, 1040,
   1050, 1060, 1070, 1080, 1090

2. £154
3. £639
4. £712
5. £439
6. £315
7. £840

The price after £100 has been added:

2. £264
3. £749
4. £822
5. £549
6. £425
7. £950

page 17
I more, I less, I0 more, I0 less

1. 2495, 2497
2. 6401, 6403
3. 3136, 3138
4. 4998, 5000
5. 5668, 5670
6. 3651, 3653
Owl 251
7. True
8. False
9. False
10. True
11. False
12. False

Block BI
page 18
Adding to I0

1. $8 + 2 = 10$
2. $4 + 6 = 10$
3. $5 + 5 = 10$
4. $9 + 1 = 10$
5. $3 + 7 = 10$
6. $7 + 3 = 10$
7. $5 + 5 = 10$
8. $6 + 4 = 10$
9. $7 + 3 = 10$
10. $3 + 7 = 10$
11. $2 + 8 = 10$
12. $1 + 9 = 10$
Owl Answers will vary. An example might be $1 + 3 + 6 = 10$.

page 19
Making I0 and 20

1. $7 + 3 = 10, 17 + 3 = 20$
2. $6 + 4 = 10, 6 + 14 = 20$
3. $6 + 4 = 10, 16 + 4 = 20$
4. $3 + 7 = 10, 13 + 7 = 20$
5. $1 + 9 = 10, 11 + 9 = 20$
6. $2 + 8 = 10, 12 + 8 = 20$
Owl 7
7. $10 - 8 = 2$
8. $10 - 5 = 5$
9. $20 - 12 = 8$
10. $20 - 11 = 9$
11. $10 - 7 = 3$
12. $20 - 18 = 2$

page 20
Making 20 and I00

1. $13 + 7 = 20$
2. $9 + 11 = 20$
3. $17 + 3 = 20$
4. $7 + 13 = 20$
5. $6 + 14 = 20$
6. $11 + 9 = 20$
7. $40 + 60 = 100$
8. $60 + 40 = 100$
9. $70 + 30 = 100$
10. $80 + 20 = 100$
11. $100 - 60 = 40$
12. $100 - 30 = 70$
Owl Answers will vary. An example might be $350 + 650 = 1000$.

page 21
Making the next I0

1. $37 + 3 = 40$
2. $26 + 4 = 30$

page 21 continued

3. $52 + 8 = 60$
4. $81 + 9 = 90$
5. $45 + 5 = 50$
6. $74 + 6 = 80$
7. $13 + 7 = 20$
8. $32 + 8 = 40$
9. $88 + 2 = 90$
10. 23p
11. $7 \times 10 - 62 = 8$
    Annie needs 8 more cherries.
Owl Answers will vary.
12. Five

page 22
Adding

1. $3 + 7 = 10, 10 + 8 = 18$
2. $4 + 6 = 10, 10 + 8 = 18$
3. $2 + 8 = 10, 10 + 9 = 19$
4. $9 + 1 = 10, 10 + 9 = 19$
5. $3 + 7 = 10, 10 + 6 = 16$
6. $5 + 5 = 10, 10 + 4 = 14$
7. $6 + 4 = 10, 10 + 5 = 15$
8. $1 + 9 = 10, 10 + 8 = 18$
9. $8 + 2 = 10, 10 + 4 = 14$
Owl Any totals between 11 and 27
10. $4p + 6p + 8p = 18p$
11. $9p + 1p + 5p = 15p$
12. $2p + 8p + 4p + 2p = 16p$
13. $7p + 3p + 7p = 17p$
14. $6p + 4p + 9p + 1p = 20p$
15. $3p + 7p + 4p = 14p$

page 23
Adding

1. $8 + 2 = 10, 10 + 6 = 16, 16 + 9 = 25$
2. $3 + 7 = 10, 10 + 8 = 18, 18 + 8 = 26$
3. $4 + 6 = 10, 10 + 9 = 19, 19 + 6 = 25$
4. $9 + 1 = 10, 10 + 9 = 19, 19 + 4 = 23$
5. $3 + 7 = 10, 10 + 5 = 15, 15 + 6 = 21$
6. $5 + 5 = 10, 10 + 4 = 14, 14 + 3 = 17$
Owl Answers will vary. An example might be 6, 6, 8 and 5.

7. $11p + 5p + 9p + 3p = 28p$
8. $12p + 8p + 5p + 2p = 27p$
9. $2p + 14p + 8p + 6p = 30p$
10. $5p + 15p + 6p + 8p = 34p$
11. $3p + 6p + 4p + 17p = 30p$
12. $3p + 16p + 8p + 5p = 32p$

page 24
Adding

1. $22p + 7p + 3p + 9p = 41p$
2. $2p + 12p + 9p + 35p + 8p = 66p$
3. $26p + 8p + 9p + 1p + 4p = 48p$
4. $6p + 4p + 11p + 7p + 5p = 33p$
5. $24 + 9 + 8 + 4 + 3 = 48, 2$
6. $£46 + £18 + £6 + £14 = £84$
7. Answers will vary. An example might be $4p + 6p + 8p + 2p + 19p = 39p$.
Owl Any number between 1p and 50p, except for the multiples of 5 (i.e. 5p, 10p, 15p …)

page 25
Adding

1. $22p + 8p + 3p + 7p + 9p = 49p$
2. $9p + 17p + 6p + 4p + 8p = 44p$
3. $17p + 5p + 24p + 19p + 3p = 68p$
4. $2p + 25p + 9p + 8p + 24p = 68p$
5. $4p + 27p + 3p + 16p + 4p = 54p$
6. $7p + 21p + 19p + 14p + 2p = 63p$
7. $25p + 8p + 4p + 25p + 9p = 71p$
8. $27p + 8p + 4p + 7p + 3p + 5p = 54p$
9. $6p + 27p + 4p + 9p + 2p = 48p$
10. $24p + 9p + 6p + 17p + 3p = 59p$
11. $18p + 9p + 8p + 4p + 23p = 62p$
12. $5p + 8p + 23p + 18p + 4p = 58p$
13. Answers will vary. If children use stamps with values of 1p, 2p, 5p, 10p and 20p the answers will be: 5, 4, 7, 6, 5, 5, 5, 5, 6, 6, 4, 6.

page 26
Sides

1. (a) 3 (b) 4 (c) 5
    (d) 3 (e) 6 (f) 5
    (g) 4 (h) 4 (i) 4
    (j) 8 (k) 7 (l) 3
    (m) 6
2. Triangles: a, d, l; pentagons: c, f; hexagons: e, m.
Owl Answers will vary.

page 27
Names of shapes

1. quadrilateral
2. hexagon
3. hexagon
4. pentagon
5. quadrilateral
6. octagon
7. pentagon
8. quadrilateral
9. heptagon
10. Answers will vary — only one example is shown here:

11. Answers will vary — only one example is shown here:

12. Answers will vary — only one example is shown here:

13. Answers will vary — only one example is shown here:

page 28
Quadrilaterals

1. Yes
2. Yes
3. Yes
4. No
5. No
6. Yes
7. No
8. Yes
9. No
Answers will vary. Possible shapes include: triangle, hexagon, pentagon, octagon.
10. Answers will vary.

page 29
Names of shapes

1. True
2. True
3. True
4. False
5. True
6. False
Owl Answers will vary.
7. (a) pentagon   (b) triangle
    (c) octagon   (d) hexagon
    (e) quadrilateral (f) triangle
    (g) hexagon
Owl Answers will vary.

page 30
Symmetry

1. Yes
2. No
3. Yes
4. No
5. No
6. Yes
7. Yes
8. Yes
9. No

page 30 continued

10. No
11. Yes
12. Yes
13. Yes
14. No
15. Yes

page 31
Symmetry

1.
2.
3.
4.
5.
6.
7.
8.
9.
10.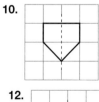
11.
12.
13.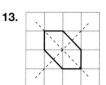
14.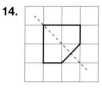
15.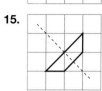
16.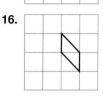
17.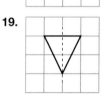
18.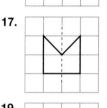
19.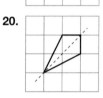
20.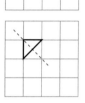

21. 'C' has 1 line of symmetry
    'L' has no lines of symmetry
    'A' has 1 line of symmetry
    'I' has 2 lines of symmetry
    'R' has no lines of symmetry
    'E' has 1 line of symmetry

page 32
Symmetrical patterns

1.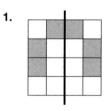

2.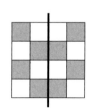

3.

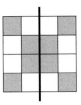

4.

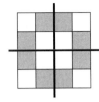

5.

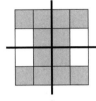

6.

7.

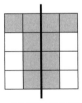

8.

9.

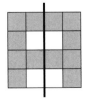

10. Answers will vary.

page 33
Lines of symmetry

1. 3

2. 4

3. 1

4. 1

5. 2

6. 3

7. 4

8. 1

9. 1

Owl Answers will vary.

Block CI
page 34
Centimetres

1. 5 cm
2. 3 cm
3. 8 cm
4. 4 cm
5. 7 cm

page 34 continued

6. 6 cm
7. 5 cm
8. 8 cm
9. 10 cm
10. 9 cm

Owl Answers will vary. An example might be two pencils measuring 6 cm and 9 cm.

page 35
Metres

1. 1 m
2. 3 m
3. 25 m
4. 6 m
5. 5 m
6. 2 m

Children will make chains up to 150 cm.

page 36
Metres and kilometres

1. 1000 m
2. 1100 m
3. 500 m
4. 1500 m
5. 2100 m
6. 3200 m
7. 5500 m
8. 4900 m
9. 10 000 m
10. 1 km 100 m
11. 2 km 300 m
12. 3 km
13. 1 km 850 m
14. 4 km 200 m
15. 1 km 700 m

Owl Answers will vary.

page 37
Metres and kilometres

1. 600 m + 600 m = 1 km 200 m
2. 900 m + 700 m = 1 km 600 m
3. 700 m + 600 m = 1 km 300 m
4. 500 m + 600 m = 1 km 100 m
5. 800 m + 500 m + 600 m = 1 km 900 m
6. 500 m + 600 m + 700 m = 1 km 800 m
7. Answers will vary.
8. Ruth walks 4 km a week.

Owl Answers will vary.

page 38
Metres and centimetres

1. more than
2. less than
3. less than
4. less than
5. less than
6. more than
7. less than
8. more than
9. more than
10. Chang jumps 31 cm further than Carrie.
11. 5 cm more fencing is needed.

page 39
Metres and centimetres

1. 1 m 34 cm
2. 1 m 86 cm
3. 2 m 35 cm
4. 2 m 8 cm
5. 1 m 94 cm
6. 3 m 84 cm
7. 0 m 75 cm
8. 3 m 2 cm
9. 0 m 96 cm

Each length written in metres:

1. 1·34 m
2. 1·86 m
3. 2·35 m
4. 2·08 m
5. 1·94 m
6. 3·84 m

7. 0·75 m
8. 3·02 m
9. 0·96 m
10. True
11. True
12. False
13. False
14. False

page 40
Metres and centimetres

1. 125 cm
2. 225 cm
3. 245 cm
4. 394 cm
5. 150 cm
6. 238 cm
7. 576 cm
8. 608 cm
9. 205 cm

To reach 10 metres, each foot needs to grow:

1. 875 cm
2. 775 cm
3. 755 cm
4. 606 cm
5. 850 cm
6. 762 cm
7. 424 cm
8. 392 cm
9. 795 cm
10. 6 cm
11. 34 cm

12. 10 cm
13. 26 cm
14. 40 cm
15. 50 cm

page 41
Tables

1. Answers will vary.

page 42
Tables

1.

People with no transport	People with one car	People with two cars	People with more than two cars	People with a van	People with a bike
3	20	12	4	7	14

2. 60
3. 7
4. 36
5. 46

Owl Answers will vary.

page 43
Tables

1. Answers will vary. Children should present their results in the tally chart using the correct marks.
2–5. Answers will vary.
Owl Answers will vary. The table may look like this:

	Wearing a sweatshirt	Wearing brown shoes	With a shirt on	With long hair	Wearing glasses	With black hair	Wearing a hairband
girls							
boys							

page 44

Tables

1. 18
2. 17
3. boys
4. bicycle
5. 126

Owl Answers will vary.

page 45

Pictograms

1. 6
2. semi-detached
3. 22
4. 28

Owl Answers will vary.

page 46

Pictograms

1. 6
2. 8
3. 8
4. green
5. yellow, purple and white
6. red
7. 28

Owl Answers will vary. An example might be the number of passengers a car has.

page 47

Pictograms

1.

CD player	cassette player	portable CD player	portable cassette player	mobile phone	television	video player	DVD player
☺☺☺☺☺☺☺☺☺	☺☺☺☺☺(	☺☺☺☺	☺☺☺(	☺	☺☺☺☺☺☺(	☺(	☺(

Owl Answers will vary. An example might be a computer or a radio.

page 48

Pictograms

1.

Type of lunch	Number of children
packed lunch with meat	⠀⠀⠀⠀⠀⠀⠀⠀⠀JHT JHT JHT III
vegetarian packed lunch	JHT IIII
school dinners with meat	JHT JHT JHT I
vegetarian school dinners	JHT JHT IIII
home	IIII

2. Answers will vary depending on the symbol chosen to represent 2 children. The pictogram may look like this:

packed lunch with meat	vegetarian packed lunch	school dinners with meat	vegetarian school dinners	home

Owl Answers will vary.

Block DI

page 49

Adding

1. $28 + 4 = 32$
2. $36 + 5 = 41$
3. $45 + 7 = 52$
4. $27 + 6 = 33$
5. $54 + 8 = 62$
6. $37 + 4 = 41$
7. $22 + 9 = 31$
8. $64 + 7 = 71$
9. $47 + 8 = 55$
10. $39 + 5 = 44$
11. $55 + 7 = 62$
12. $24 + 8 = 32$

Owl Answers will vary. Numbers should end in 6, for example, 36, 46, 56.

page 50

Adding

1. $27 + 7 = 34$
2. $84 + 8 = 92$
3. $47 + 6 = 53$
4. $55 + 8 = 63$
5. $54 + 8 = 62$
6. $65 + 7 = 72$
7. $73 + 8 = 81$
8. $36 + 5 = 41$
9. $48 + 4 = 52$
10. $46 + 7 = 53$
11. $37 + 6 = 43$
12. $52 + 8 = 60$
13. $38 + 4 = 42$
14. $45 + 6 = 51$
15. $39 + 6 = 45$

page 50 continued

16. 43 + 8 = 51
17. 54 + 7 = 61
Owl This is only true when the other number is even, for example 2 + 2 = 4.

page 5I
Adding

1. 75 + 7 = 82
2. 68 + 4 = 72
3. 37 + 8 = 45
4. 49 + 2 = 51
5. 26 + 6 = 32
6. 55 + 8 = 63
7. 36 + 6 + 8 = 50
8. 148 + 8 + 6 = 162
Owl Answers will vary.

page 52
Adding

1. 174 + 7 = 181
2. 163 + 7 = 170
3. 246 + 5 = 251
4. 86 + 5 = 91
5. 97 + 4 = 101
6. 257 + 6 = 263
7. 126 + 8 = 134
8. 256 + 6 = 262
9. 136 cm + 5 cm = 141 cm
10. 148 cm + 6 cm = 154 cm
11. 218 cm + 8 cm = 226 cm
12. 192 cm + 9 cm = 201 cm
13. 365 cm + 6 cm = 371 cm
14. 228 cm + 4 cm = 232 cm
15. 333 cm + 8 cm = 341 cm
16. 145 cm + 6 cm = 151 cm
Owl 7, 6, 9, 11, 4, 8, 7, 6

page 53
Taking away

1. 35 – 5 = 30
2. 46 – 6 = 40
3. 52 – 2 = 50
4. 64 – 4 = 60
5. 72 – 3 = 69
6. 85 – 6 = 79
7. 65 – 6 = 59
8. 74 – 4 = 70
9. 64 – 5 = 59
10. 53 – 4 = 49
11. 85 – 7 = 78
12. 71 – 6 = 65
13. 68 – 9 = 59
14. 82 – 6 = 76
Owl 6

page 54
Taking away

1. 42 – 4 = 38
2. 53 – 6 = 47
3. 72 – 5 = 67
4. 64 – 4 = 60
5. 51 – 3 = 48
6. 72 – 4 = 68
7. 34 cm – 5 cm = 29 cm
8. 52 cm – 4 cm = 48 cm
9. 63 cm – 5 cm = 58 cm
10. 41 cm – 3 cm = 38 cm
11. 55 cm – 6 cm = 49 cm
12. 44 cm – 5 cm = 39 cm
Owl Answers will vary. An example might be 80 – 5 = 75.

page 55
Taking away

1. 75p – 5p = 70p
2. 83p – 4p = 79p
3. 62p – 5p = 57p
4. 64p – 5p = 59p
5. 72p – 4p = 68p
6. 91p – 3p = 88p
7. 34 – 8 – 7 = 19
8. 62p – 5p – 4p – 12p = 41p
Owl Answers will vary.

page 56
Taking away

1. $133 - 5 = 128$
2. $168 - 5 = 163$
3. $127 - 6 = 121$
4. $272 - 4 = 268$
5. $366 - 8 = 358$
6. $428 - 3 = 425$

Owl Answers will vary. There are 24 possible variations, for example $345 - 6$.

7. It is better to spend £10 per week. The other option leaves you with no money in week 7.

page 57
Half past, quarter past, quarter to

1. D
2. A
3. F
4. E
5. B
6. C

half past 2, quarter past 4, quarter to 6, quarter past 7, 9 o'clock, quarter past 10

7. 8 o'clock
8. half past 4
9. quarter past 6
10. quarter to 12

page 58
5 minutes

1. 15 minutes
2. 35 minutes
3. 5 minutes
4. 20 minutes
5. 25 minutes
6. 10 minutes
7. 35 minutes
8. 55 minutes

Number of minutes before 12:

1. 45 minutes
2. 20 minutes

3. 25 minutes
4. 25 minutes
5. 35 minutes
6. 5 minutes
7. 0 minutes
8. 5 minutes

Owl 3 hours 20 minutes

9. 5 minutes
10. 15 minutes
11. 25 minutes
12. 45 minutes
13. 10 minutes
14. 35 minutes

page 59
5 minutes

1. 5 past 4
2. 10 past 7
3. 25 past 8
4. 10 to 6

Owl Answers will vary. Possible answers include 1:21, 3:53, 10:01 or 23:32.

5. 5:45
6. 3:05
7. 4:20
8. 2:55
9. 11:10
10. 12:40
11. 11:30
12. 00:20

page 60
5 minutes

1. 15 minutes
2. 45 minutes
3. 35 minutes
4. 40 minutes
5. 25 minutes
6. 35 minutes
7. 40 minutes
8. 10:40
9. 7:50

Owl Answers will vary.

page 6I

5 minutes

1. quarter to 3
2. quarter past 7
3. half past 8
4. 4 o'clock
5. half past 10
6. quarter past 2
7. 4:30
8. 7:00
9. 11:30
10. 11:00
11. 3:45
12. 9:45
13. 1:15
14. 9:00
15. 7:15
Owl Three times

page 62

5 minutes

1. twenty five past 12
2. quarter past 10
3. half past 2
4. ten past 3
5. five past 9
6. twenty to 5
Owl ten past 3 and twenty to 5
Answers will vary. An example might be ten to 9.
7. 8:50
8. 7:35
9. 7:45
10. 8:45
11. 8:25
12. 7:05

page 63

5 minutes

1. twenty five past 6
2. quarter past 9
3. twenty to 2
4. twenty to 12
5. ten to 2
6. ten to 3
Owl ten to 8, five past 11, 3 o'clock, five to 1, five to 3, ten to 5
7. 3:25
8. 5:05
9. 7:20
10. 6:50
11. 5:50
12. 4:30

page 64

5 minutes

1. 9:40, 10:05, 9:55, 10:25, 10:10, 10:10, 11:30, 11:10, 10:45, 11:05
2. The match finishes at 5:05.
3. Beth's alarm went off at 7:55.
Owl Answers will vary.

Block EI

page 65

Multiplying

1. $5 \times 3 = 15$
2. $4 \times 5 = 20$
3. $3 \times 6 = 18$
4. $7 \times 2 = 14$
5. $4 \times 10 = 40$
6. $5 \times 4 = 20$
Owl $12 + 12$, $8 + 8 + 8$, $6 + 6 + 6 + 6$, $4 + 4 + 4 + 4 + 4 + 4$, $3 + 3 + 3 + 3 + 3 + 3 + 3 + 3$, $2 + 2 + 2 + 2 + 2 + 2 + 2 + 2 + 2 + 2 + 2 + 2$
7. $4 \times 3 = 12$
8. $6 \times 2 = 12$
9. $3 \times 5 = 15$
10. $5 \times 4 = 20$
11. $2 \times 6 = 12$
12. $6 \times 3 = 18$

page 66
Multiplying

1. $3 \times 4 = 12$
2. $4 \times 5 = 20$
3. $2 \times 6 = 12$
4. $2 \times 7 = 14$
5. $7 \times 3 = 21$
6. $6 \times 4 = 24$
Owl 24p, 40p, 24p, 28p, 42p, 48p
7. $5 \times 4 = 20$
8. $2 \times 2 = 4$
9. $3 \times 5 = 15$
10. $4 \times 6 = 24$
11. $7 \times 1 = 7$
12. $6 \times 3 = 18$
13. $8 \times 5 = 40$
14. $4 \times 4 = 16$
15. Answers will vary.

page 67
Multiplying and dividing

1. $6 \div 3 = 2$
2. $10 \div 2 = 5$
3. $12 \div 4 = 3$
4. $20 \div 5 = 4$

Multiplications for each set:
1. $2 \times 3 = 6$
2. $5 \times 2 = 10$
3. $3 \times 4 = 12$
4. $4 \times 5 = 20$
5. $14 \div 2 = 7$
6. $9 \div 3 = 3$
7. $15 \div 5 = 3$
8. $20 \div 4 = 5$
9. $10 \div 2 = 5$
10. $24 \div 6 = 4$
11. $70 \div 10 = 7$
12. $25 \div 5 = 5$
13. $4 \times 3 = 12$, $12 \div 3 = 4$
14. $2 \times 4 = 8$, $8 \div 4 = 2$
15. $3 \times 5 = 15$, $15 \div 5 = 3$
16. $5 \times 2 = 10$, $10 \div 2 = 5$

page 68
Multiplying and dividing

1. $6 \times 4 = 24$ cabbages
2. $24 \div 6 = 4p$ per cake
3. $30 \div 6 = 5$ rows
4. $14 \times 4 = 56 = 3$ loaves
Owl Answers will vary.
5. True
6. False
7. True
8. False

page 69
Twos

1. 10, 12, 14, 16
2. 14, 16, 18, 20, 22
3. 0, 2, 4, 6
4. 6, 8, 10, 12, 14
   18, 20, 22, 24,…
   24, 26, 28, 30,…
5. $4 \times 2 = 8$
6. $5 \times 2 = 10$
7. $3 \times 2 = 6$
8. $6 \times 2 = 12$
Owl $8 \times 3 = 24$, $10 \times 3 = 30$, $6 \times 3 = 18$, $12 \times 3 = 36$

page 70
Multiplying by 2

1. 12
2. 8
3. 2
4. 14
5. 6
6. 18
Owl Answers will vary, however all positions marked should be multiples of 20.
7. $4 \times 2 = 8$
8. $7 \times 2 = 14$
9. $3 \times 2 = 6$
10. $3 \times 2 = 6$

page 70 continued

11. $8 \times 2 = 16$
12. $9 \times 2 = 18$
13. $5 \times 2 = 10$
14. $10 \times 2 = 20$
15. $6 \times 2 = 12$
16. $3 \times 2 = 6$
17. $2 \times 2 = 4$
18. $9 \times 2 = 18$

page 71
Dividing by 2

1. $8 \div 2 = 4$
2. $14 \div 2 = 7$
3. $10 \div 2 = 5$
4. $6 \div 2 = 3$
5. $20 \div 2 = 10$
6. $16 \div 2 = 8$
7. $18 \div 2 = 9$
8. $4 \div 2 = 2$
9. $12 \div 2 = 6$
Owl 18 boots or 9 pairs
10. $10 \div 2 = 5$
11. $4 \div 2 = 2$
12. $14 \div 2 = 7$
13. $6 \div 2 = 3$
14. $12 \div 2 = 6$
15. $18 \div 2 = 9$

page 72
Multiplying and dividing by 2

1. $3 \times 2p = 6p$
2. $8 \times 2p = 16p$
3. $4 \times 2p = 8p$
4. $9 \times 2p = 18p$
5. $6 \times 2p = 12p$
6. $2 \times 2p = 4p$
7. $10 \times 2p = 20p$
8. $7 \times 2p = 14p$
9. $17 \times 2p = 34p$
10. True
11. True
12. False
13. 8p change
14. 9 pairs
15. 9
16. 24

page 73
Fractions

1. $\frac{1}{2}$
2. $\frac{1}{3}$
3. $\frac{1}{2}$
4. $\frac{1}{4}$
5. $\frac{1}{2}$
6. $\frac{1}{4}$
7. $\frac{1}{8}$
8. $\frac{1}{8}$
9. $\frac{1}{2}$
10. $\frac{1}{8}$
11. $\frac{1}{3}$
12. $\frac{2}{8}$
Owl 4, 8
13. 4, 2, 1
14. 8, 4, 2
15. 5, 2

page 74
Fractions

1. $\frac{1}{4}$ of 16 = 4
2. $\frac{1}{2}$ of 8 = 4
3. $\frac{1}{3}$ of 15 = 5
4. $\frac{1}{5}$ of 10 = 2
5. $\frac{1}{4}$ of 12 = 3
6. $\frac{1}{3}$ of 9 = 3
7. $\frac{1}{10}$ of 20 = 2
8. $\frac{1}{8}$ of 16 = 2
9. $\frac{1}{6}$ of 18 = 3
Owl Answers will vary. An example might be $\frac{1}{2}$ of 16 = 8.

10. $\frac{1}{2}$ of 14 = 7

11. $\frac{1}{3}$ of 12 = 4

12. $\frac{1}{4}$ of 8 = 2

13. $\frac{1}{5}$ of 15 = 3

14. $\frac{1}{6}$ of 18 = 3

15. $\frac{1}{8}$ of 16 = 2

16. $\frac{1}{10}$ of 70 = 7

17. $\frac{1}{3}$ of 21 = 7

18. $\frac{1}{4}$ of 32 = 8

page 75
Fractions

1. 30 seconds

2. 16 hours

3. 12 cars

4. 5 children prefer plain crisps.

5. $\frac{1}{2}$ of 20 = 10

6. $\frac{1}{3}$ of 15 = 5

7. $\frac{1}{10}$ of 40 = 4

8. $\frac{1}{4}$ of 24 = 6

9. $\frac{1}{5}$ of 20 = 4

10. $\frac{1}{3}$ of 21 = 7

Owl $\frac{1}{2}$ slice → £3, $\frac{1}{4}$ slice → £1·50, $\frac{1}{6}$ slice → £1, $\frac{1}{8}$ slice → 75p

page 76
Fractions

1. True

2. True

3. False

Owl Answers will vary.

4. $\frac{1}{4}$ of B = 10p

5. $\frac{1}{2}$ of E = 33p

6. $\frac{1}{3}$ of C = 12p

7. $\frac{1}{2}$ of A = 25p

8. $\frac{1}{3}$ of D = 20p

9. $\frac{1}{5}$ of A = 10p

10. $\frac{1}{8}$ of B = 5p

11. $\frac{1}{6}$ of C = 6p

12. $\frac{1}{6}$ of D = 10p

page 77
Doubling and halving

1. double 3 = 6

2. double 5 = 10

3. double 6 =12

4. double 4 = 8

5. double 8 = 16

6. double 7 = 14

7. double 9 = 18

8. double 2 = 4

9. double 10 = 20

Owl Answers will vary. It might be difficult to halve the number of people in the class if this number is odd.

10. double 4 = 8

11. half of 8 = 4

12. double 9 = 18

13. half of 16 = 8

14. double 7 = 14

15. half of 12 = 6

16. double 3 = 6

17. half of 14 = 7

18. double 8 = 16

page 78
Doubling and halving

1. 10p

2. 40p

3. 80p

4. 30p

5. 60p

6. 50p

7. 70p

8. 90p

9. 100p

Owl Total coins = £2·65, total answers = £5·30.

10. 20p

page 78 continued

11. 30p
12. 15p
13. 35p
14. 25p
15. 45p
Owl 11, 14 and 15 or 10, 13 and 15

page 79
Doubling and halving

1. double 12 = 24
2. double 14 = 28
3. double 13 = 26
4. double 16 = 32
5. double 18 = 36
6. double 15 = 30

7.

In	13	15	17	12	19	14	18	16
Out	26	30	34	24	38	28	36	32

8.

In	28	32	26	38	34	24	36	30
Out	14	16	13	19	17	12	18	15

9. Answers will vary.

page 80
Doubling and halving

1. half of 32 = 16
2. twice 17 = 34
3. double of double 7 = 28
4. half of half of 100 = 25

5. half of double 15 = 15
6. double half of 70 = 70
7. half of 90p = 45p
8. double 45p = 90p
   Anil would need 10p more.

9.

22	36	24		44	72	48
34	26	32		68	52	64
28	38	30		56	76	60

10.

60	140	40
120	20	180
100	160	80

120	280	80
240	40	360
200	320	160

11.

50	130	90
150	10	30
70	170	110

100	260	180
300	20	60
140	340	220

12.

42	84	66
104	28	46
86	68	108

84	168	132
208	56	92
172	136	216

Textbook 2

Block A2

page 3
Rounding

1. $16 \rightarrow 20$
2. $23 \rightarrow 20$
3. $46 \rightarrow 50$
4. $43 \rightarrow 40$
5. $37 \rightarrow 40$
6. $51 \rightarrow 50$
7. $34 \rightarrow 30$
8. $22 \rightarrow 20$
9. $48 \rightarrow 50$
10. $64 \rightarrow 60$
11. $12 \rightarrow 10$
12. $73 \rightarrow 70$
13. $11 \rightarrow 10$
14. $82 \rightarrow 80$
15. $74 \rightarrow 70$
Owl Answers will vary. An example might be numbers which round to 50: 45, 46, 47, 48, 49, 51, 52, 53 and 54.

page 4
Rounding

1. $42 \rightarrow 40$
2. $86 \rightarrow 90$
3. $27 \rightarrow 30$
4. $95 \rightarrow 100$
5. $12 \rightarrow 10$
6. $54 \rightarrow 50$
7. $21p \rightarrow 20p$
8. $42p \rightarrow 40p$
9. $74p \rightarrow 70p$
10. $31p \rightarrow 30p$
11. $68p \rightarrow 70p$
12. $52p \rightarrow 50p$
13. $57p \rightarrow 60p$
14. $33p \rightarrow 30p$
Owl 16

page 5
Rounding

1. $24 \rightarrow 20$
2. $38 \rightarrow 40$
3. $81 \rightarrow 80$
4. $66 \rightarrow 70$
5. $74 \rightarrow 70$
6. $53 \rightarrow 50$
7. $46 \rightarrow 50$
8. $28 \rightarrow 30$
9. $31 \rightarrow 30$
10. $69 \rightarrow 70$
11. $22 \rightarrow 20$
12. $53 \rightarrow 50$
13. $61 \rightarrow 60$
14. $33 \rightarrow 30$
15. $38 \rightarrow 40$
Owl Answers will vary.

page 6
Rounding

1. $142 \rightarrow 140$
2. $64 \rightarrow 60$
3. $173 \rightarrow 170$
4. $273 \rightarrow 270$
5. $89 \rightarrow 90$
6. $385 \rightarrow 390$
7. $75 \rightarrow 80$
8. $496 \rightarrow 500$
9. $517 \rightarrow 520$
10. £1·34 $\rightarrow$ £1·30
11. £2·17 $\rightarrow$ £2·20
12. £1·21 $\rightarrow$ £1·20
13. £1·42 $\rightarrow$ £1·40
14. £1·75 $\rightarrow$ £1·80
15. £1·82 $\rightarrow$ £1·80
16. £1·87 $\rightarrow$ £1·90
17. £1·33 $\rightarrow$ £1·30
18. £1·58 $\rightarrow$ £1·60
Owl £1, £2, £1, £1, £2, £2, £2, £1, £2
40 amounts round down.

page 7

Comparing numbers

1. 435, 443
2. 82, 88
3. 726, 762
4. 608, 612
5. 541, 548
6. 312, 321
7. Any number from 463 to 483
8. Any number from 817 to 860
9. Any number from 346 to 353
10. 320
11. Any number from 211 to 221
12. Any number from 506 to 549
13. 427
14. Any number from 328 to 371
15. Any number from 617 to 660
Owl 19

page 8

Comparing numbers

1. 610, 635
2. 350, 380
3. 420, 450
4. 725, 740
5. 555, 565
6. 215, 260

A number between the given dates:
1. Any number from 611 to 634
2. Any number from 351 to 379
3. Any number from 421 to 449
4. Any number from 726 to 739
5. Any number from 556 to 564
6. Any number from 216 to 259
7. Any number from AD44 to AD409
8. Any number from £491 to £499
9. A number in the region of 547
10. Any number from 366 to 371
Owl Answers will vary.

page 9

Ordering numbers

1. 365, 370, 381
2. 402, 408, 412
3. 502, 524, 550
4. 891, 914, 920
5. 734, 745, 754
6. 696, 966, 969
7. 565 cm
   Any length from 466 cm to 564 cm
8. 724 cm
   Any length from 625 cm to 723 cm
9. 802 cm
   Any length from 703 cm to 801 cm
10. 399 cm
    Any length from 300 cm to 398 cm
11. 675 cm
    Any length from 576 cm to 674 cm
12. 1098 cm
    Any length from 999 cm to 1097 cm
13. 750 cm
    Any length from 651 cm to 749 cm
14. 532 cm
    Any length from 433 cm to 531 cm
Owl Any pair from:
910 and 820
820 and 730
730 and 640
640 and 550
550 and 460
460 and 370
370 and 280
280 and 190

page 10

Ordering numbers

1. 456 g, 460 g
   457 g, 458 g or 459 g
2. 380 g, 410 g
   Any weight from 381 g to 409 g
3. 588 g, 590 g
   589 g
4. 989 g, 999 g
   Any weight from 990 g to 998 g

5. 199 g, 202 g
200 g or 201 g

6. 646 g, 664 g
Any weight from 647 g to 663 g

7. 347, 348, 374, 378, 384, 387, 437,
438, 473, 478, 483, 487, 734, 738,
743, 748, 783, 784, 834, 837, 843,
847, 873, 874

8. £4·59, £4·99
Any two prices from £4·60 to £4·98

9. £6·85, £6·99
Any two prices from £6·86 to £6·98

10. £9·95, £9·98
£9·96 and £9·97

11. £3·54, £4·35
Any two prices from £3·55 to £4·34

12. £2·50, £2·99
Any two prices from £2·51 to £2·98

13. £3·42, £3·45
£3·43 and £3·44

page II
Counting in I0s

1. 70, 80, 90
2. 40, 50, 60
3. 100, 110, 120
4. 80, 90, 100
5. 150, 160, 170
6. 180, 190, 200
7. 360, 370, 380
8. 590, 600, 610
9. 920, 930, 940
10. 5
11. 7
12. 18
13. 14
14. 16
15. 19
Owl
10. 10
11. 14
12. 36
13. 28

14. 32
15. 38

page I2
Counting in I00s

1. 3
2. 9
3. 6
4. 8
5. 10
6. 12
7. 1000 pins
8. 1100 pins
9. 1500 pins
10. 1900 pins
11. 1800 pins
12. 1200 pins
Owl 10 000 boxes

page I3
Counting in 50s

1. 150
2. 300
3. 400
4. 250
5. 350
6. 200
7. 450
8. 650
9.

Number of bags	10	15	13	18	7	22	17	39
Number of tacks	500	750	650	900	350	1100	850	1950

10. £8·50
Owl About 38 or 39 years

page I4
Counting in I00s and 50s

1. 8 bags, 67p left, £8·67
2. 3 bags, 42p left, £3·42
3. 6 bags, 50p left, £6·50

page 14 continued

4. 9 bags, £9·00
5. 13 bags, 41p left, £13·41
6. 17 bags, 50p left, £17·50
7. 18 bags, 40p left, £18·40
8. 26 bags, 73p left, £26·73
9. 14 bags, 37p left, £14·37
10. 9 bags, 56p left, £9·56

Each bag only contains 50p:
1. 17 bags, 17p left
2. 6 bags, 42p left
3. 13 bags
4. 18 bags
5. 26 bags, 41p left
6. 35 bags
7. 36 bags, 40p left
8. 53 bags, 23p left
9. 28 bags, 37p left
10. 19 bags, 6p left
11. 2600 g or 2·6 kg
Owl 10th number: 282
100th number: 2532

page 15
Counting in 2s

1. 12, 14, 16, 18
2. 9, 11, 13, 15
3. 18, 20, 22, 24
4. 21, 23, 25, 27
5. 40, 42, 44, 46
6. 49, 51, 53, 55
7. 27, 29, 31, 33
8. 24, 26, 28, 30
9. 30, 32, 34, 36
10. 11, 13, 15, 17
11.

b 1	r 2	b 3	r 4	b 5	r 6	b 7	r 8	b 9
r 10	b 11	r 12	b 13	r 14	b 15	r 16	b 17	r 18
b 19	r 20	b 21	r 22	b 23	r 24	b 25	r 26	b 27
r 28	b 29	r 30	b 31	r 32	b 33	r 34	b 35	r 36
b 37	r 38	b 39	r 40	b 41	r 42	b 43	r 44	b 45
r 46	b 47	r 48	b 49	r 50	b 51	r 52	b 53	r 54

r = red   b = blue

Owl

17	r 16	15	r 14	13
r 18	5	r 4	3	r 12
19	r 6	1	r 2	11
r 20	7	r 8	9	r 10
21	r 22	23	r 24	25

r = red

page 16
Counting in 2s, even and odd

1. 25, 27, 29, 31, 33, 35, 37
2. 40, 42, 44, 46, 48, 50, 52
3. 1, 3, 5, 7, 9, 11, 13
4. 15, 17, 19, 21, 23, 25, 27
5. 10, 12, 14, 16, 18, 20, 22
6. 26, 28, 30, 32, 34, 36, 38
7. 35, 37, 39, 41, 43, 45, 47
8. 19, 21, 23, 25, 27, 29, 31
9. 6, 10, 38, 64, 72
10. 43, 49, 51, 57
11. 27
Owl 124, excluding 250 and 500

page 17
Counting in 2s, even and odd

1. 88 even
2. 31 odd
3. 50 even
4. 64 even
5. 30 even
6. 47 odd
7. 53 odd
8. 44 even

1. 88 even: half = 44
2. 31 odd: double = 62
3. 50 even: half = 25
4. 64 even: half = 32
5. 30 even: half = 15
6. 47 odd: double = 94
7. 53 odd: double = 106
8. 44 even: half = 22

Textbook 2

9. False
10. True
11. True

page 18
Counting in 2s, even and odd

Even numbers:
1. 66, 68, 70 or 72
2. Any even number from 174 to 238
3. 504, 506, 508 or 510
4. 412 or 414
5. 202
6. 316
7. 400
8. 86

Odd numbers:
1. 65, 67, 69 or 71
2. Any odd number from 173 to 239
3. 503, 505, 507, 509 or 511
4. 413
5. 201 or 203
6. 315
7. 399
8. 85 or 87
9. Answers will vary. Children may suggest a variety of possible explanations for the length of the chains. An example might be that large numbers make longer chains.

Owl Answers will vary. An example might be $6 + 8 + 9 + 7 = 30$.

Block B2

page 19
Adding to 10, adding to 100

1. $3 + 7 = 10$
2. $2 + 8 = 10$
3. $1 + 9 = 10$
4. $9 + 1 = 10$
5. $8 + 2 = 10$
6. $6 + 4 = 10$

7. $30 + 70 = 100$
8. $50 + 50 = 100$
9. $40 + 60 = 100$
10. $20 + 80 = 100$
11. $70 + 30 = 100$
12. $10 + 90 = 100$
13. $60 + 40 = 100$
14. $80 + 20 = 100$

Owl 64 and 36

page 20
Adding to 100, adding to 1000

1. $300 + 700 = 1000$
2. $200 + 800 = 1000$
3. $100 + 900 = 1000$
4. $900 + 100 = 1000$
5. $800 + 200 = 1000$
6. $600 + 400 = 1000$
7. $65 + 35 = 100$
8. $15 + 85 = 100$
9. $25 + 75 = 100$
10. $55 + 45 = 100$
11. $35 + 65 = 100$
12. $45 + 55 = 100$
13. $75 + 25 = 100$
14. $85 + 15 = 100$

Owl Answers will vary.

page 21
Adding to 100

1. $£1 - 65p = 35p$
2. $£1 - 85p = 15p$
3. $£1 - 25p = 75p$
4. $£1 - 15p = 85p$
5. $£1 - 60p = 40p$
6. $£1 - 95p = 5p$
7. $£1 - 45p = 55p$
8. $£1 - 20p = 80p$
9. 97p
10. £35, £55
11. 65 years

Owl 11, from $0 + 100$ to $50 + 50$

page 22
Adding to £1, adding to next £1

1. 55p + 45p = £1
   80p + 20p = £1
   68p + 32p = £1
   60p + 40p = £1
2. £2 − £1·10 = 90p
3. £2 − £1·85 = 15p
4. £2 − £1·60 = 40p
5. £2 − £1·35 = 65p
6. £2 − £1·45 = 55p
7. £2 − £1·15 = 85p
8. £2 − £1·20 = 80p
9. £2 − £1·70 = 30p

Owl Answers will vary.

page 23
Adding to 100, adding to 1000

1. 60 + 40 = 100
2. 80 + 20 = 100
3. 70 + 30 = 100
4. 90 + 10 = 100
5. 55 + 45 = 100
6. 40 + 60 = 100
7. 10 + 90 = 100
8. 30 + 70 = 100
9. 700 + 300 = 1000
10. 600 + 400 = 1000
11. 300 + 700 = 1000
12. 400 + 600 = 1000
13. 800 + 200 = 1000
14. 200 + 800 = 1000
15. 500 + 500 = 1000
16. 900 + 100 = 1000

Owl Answers will vary.

page 24
Adding to 100, adding to next 100

1. 390 + 10 = 400 cm
2. 380 + 20 = 400 cm
3. 360 + 40 = 400 cm
4. 340 + 60 = 400 cm
5. 330 + 70 = 400 cm
6. 320 + 80 = 400 cm
7. 80 m, 250 m
8. 480 + 20 = 500
9. 120 + 80 = 200
10. 360 + 40 = 400
11. 270 + 30 = 300
12. 460 + 40 = 500
13. 350 + 50 = 400

Owl Answers will vary.

page 25
Adding to next 100, adding to next £1

1. 790 + 10 = 800 m
2. 780 + 20 = 800 m
3. 760 + 40 = 800 m
4. 740 + 60 = 800 m
5. 730 + 70 = 800 m
6. 720 + 80 = 800 m
7. 450 + 50 = 500, 540 + 60 = 600,
   560 + 40 = 600, 650 + 50 = 700
8. £3·60 + 40p = £4
9. £3·30 + 70p = £4
10. £4·80 + 20p = £5
11. £4·20 + 80p = £5

page 26
Adding to next 100

1. 335 + 65 = 400
2. 625 + 75 = 700
3. 555 + 45 = 600
4. 465 + 35 = 500
5. 1300 + 700 = 2000
6. 815 + 85 = 900
7. 4800 + 200 = 5000
8. 1300 + 100 = 1400
9. 450 + 550 = 1000
10. 285 + 15 = 300
11. 65p, £6·65
12. £1·15
13. £4, £6
14. Matt

Owl 80 and 20 or 160 and 40

page 27
Prisms

1. Yes
2. Yes
3. Yes
4. No
5. Yes
6. Yes
7. No
8. No
9. Yes

The end-faces of each prism:

1. Triangles
2. Pentagons
3. Squares
4. Not a prism
5. Hexagons
6. Circle
7. Not a prism
8. Not a prism
9. Octagons

Owl A cylinder rolls.

page 28
Prisms

1. 5 rectangles, 2 pentagons
2. 4 rectangles, 2 trapeziums
3. 4 rectangles, 2 squares
4. 6 rectangles, 2 hexagons
5. 8 rectangles, 2 octagons
6. 3 rectangles, 2 triangles
7.

Prism	Faces
Triangular prism	5
Quadrilateral prism	6
Pentagonal prism	7
Hexagonal prism	8
Heptagonal prism	9
Octagonal prism	10

Owl A 10-sided polygon

page 29
Prisms

1. Yes
2. Yes
3. No
4. No
5. Yes
6. Yes

Owl Answers will vary.

page 30
Flat and curved faces

1. a, d, e, g, h, i
2. j
3. b, c, f
4. j
5. none
6. a, d, e, g, h, i
7. a, e, g
8. b, c, f, j
9. i, d

Owl Answers will vary.

page 31
3D shapes

1. (a) cone
   (b) sphere
   (c) cube
   (d) cylinder
   (e) cuboid
   (f) pyramid
   (g) cuboid
   (h) cube
   (i) cuboid
2. 2
3. 3
4. 1
5. 1
6. 1
7. 6
8. 1

page 3I continued

9.
(a) 2 (b) 1
(c) 6 (d) 3
(e) 6 (f) 5
(g) 6 (h) 6
(i) 6

10.
(a) 1 (b) 0
(c) 8 (d) 0
(e) 8 (f) 5
(g) 8 (h) 8
(i) 8

11.
(a) 1 (b) 0
(c) 12 (d) 2
(e) 12 (f) 8
(g) 12 (h) 12
(i) 12

Owl Answers will vary. Children may draw a net of a standard cuboid, or they may include the extra flaps from the top and bottom of a cereal box.

page 32
3D shapes

shape	b	f	d	a	c	e
faces	4	5	5	6	7	8

shape	b	f	d	a	c	e
edges	6	8	9	12	15	18

shape	b	f	d	a	c	e
vertices	4	5	6	8	10	12

Owl The shapes with an odd number of faces are the pentagonal and triangular prisms and the pyramid. Shapes with an odd number of faces are prisms based on 2D shapes with an odd number of sides.

page 33
3D shapes

1. True
2. False
3. True
4. True
5. True
6. True
7. False
8. False – it could have squares
9. False
10. False
11. True
12. 1 square
4 triangles
13. 2 circles
1 rectangle
14. 2 triangles
3 rectangles
15. 6 squares
16. 1 pentagon
5 triangles
17. 2 hexagons
6 rectangles

Block C2

page 34
Litres and millilitres

1. less
2. more
3. equal to
4. equal to
5. equal to
6. less
7. less
8. more
9. equal to

Owl
1. 200 ml less
2. 200 ml more
3. equal to
4. equal to
5. equal to
6. 250 ml less
7. 400 ml less
8. 350 ml more
9. equal to

10. 1000 ml
11. 3000 ml
12. 5000 ml
13. 500 ml

page 35
Litres and millilitres

1. 800 ml
2. 300 ml
3. 500 ml
4. 700 ml
5. 200 ml
6. 900 ml
7. 400 ml
8. 600 ml
   Total 4400 ml
9. 1 l 200 ml
10. 2 l 500 ml
11. 3 l 100 ml
12. 0 l 600 ml
13. 4 l 0 ml
14. 0 l 500 ml
15. 7 l 200 ml
16. 3 l 500 ml
Owl Milk, lemonade, orange juice, etc.

page 36
Litres and millilitres

1. 1000 ml
2. 1100 ml
3. 1500 ml
4. 2400 ml
5. 5900 ml
6. 3500 ml
7. 1800 ml
8. 2500 ml
9. 4700 ml
10. 500 ml
11. 6300 ml
12. 1250 ml
Owl 1000 ml, 2400 ml, 1800 ml

13. $\frac{1}{2}$ l, 800 ml, 1200 ml, $1\frac{1}{2}$ l, 2 l
14. 50 ml, 90 ml, 300 ml, $\frac{1}{2}$ l, $1\frac{1}{2}$ l
15. $6 \times 250\,ml = 1500\,ml$
    $4 \times 500\,ml = 2000\,ml$
    $12 \times 200\,ml = 2400\,ml$

page 37
Litres and millilitres

1. True
2. True
3. False
4. True
5. 24 jugfuls
6. 100 cupfuls
7. 3600 ml
8. 100 tablespoons
9. 60 ml
10. 4 tins
Owl Answers will vary.

page 38
Days and hours

1. Friday
2. Tuesday
3. Wednesday
4. Sunday
5. Monday
6. Saturday
7. Thursday
   Monday, Tuesday, Wednesday,
   Thursday, Friday, Saturday, Sunday
8. 8 o'clock
9. 10 o'clock
10. midnight/12 o'clock
11. 4 o'clock
12. 9 o'clock
13. midday/12 o'clock
14. 1 o'clock
15. 4 o'clock
16. 2 o'clock
Owl 18 hours

page 39
Minutes and hours

1.   60 minutes
2.   120 minutes
3.   80 minutes
4.   130 minutes
5.   90 minutes
6.   170 minutes
7.   1 hour 20 minutes
8.   1 hour
9.   2 hours
10. 1 hour 15 minutes
11. $\frac{1}{2}$ hour or 0 hours 30 minutes
12. 3 hours

Owl
7.   8 km
8.   6 km
9.   12 km
10. $7\frac{1}{2}$ km
11. 3 km
12. 18 km
13. 80 minutes or 1 hour 20 minutes
14. 5 hours 10 minutes

page 40
Minutes and hours

1.   60 seconds
2.   120 seconds
3.   90 seconds
4.   130 seconds
5.   75 seconds
6.   210 seconds
7.   1 minute 20 seconds
8.   1 minute 30 seconds
9.   1 minute 40 seconds
10. 2 minutes
11. 2 minutes 30 seconds
12. 1 minute 25 seconds
13. 1 minute 12 seconds
14. 2 minutes 10 seconds
15. 2 minutes 25 seconds
Owl Answers will vary.
16. 356 seconds or 5 minutes 56 seconds

page 41
Hours, minutes and seconds

1.   1 hour 30 minutes
2.   2 hours 20 minutes
3.   2 hours 40 minutes
4.   168 hours
5.   86 400 seconds
6.   False
7.   True
8.   True
9.   True

page 42
Frequency tables

1.   Chocolate bars
2.   Rice cakes
3.   Cakes
4.   4
5.   6
6.   32
7.   26
8.   False
9.   True
10. False
Owl Answers will vary. Children's tables should be similar to the one below.

page 43
Frequency tables

1.

Favourite pastimes	Votes
board games	96
cards	4
dominoes	28
quiz games	57
word games	54

2.   24
3.   32
4.   Board games, quiz games and word games
5.   Dominoes and cards

Owl Answers will vary. Children's tables should be similar to question 1.

page 44
Frequency tables

1. John
2. Abdul
3. Matthew
4. Sean
Owl Answers will vary but should reflect ethnic mix and regional influences.
5.

Frequency of classroom furniture				
chairs	drawers	tables	windows	shelves

The information in children's tables will vary depending on their classroom.

page 45
Bar graphs

1. Fantasy adventures
2. Historical stories
3. Stories about everyday life
4. 12
5. 4
6. 10
Owl 32 children had 1 vote
16 children had 2 votes

page 46
Frequency tables

1. Cardiff
2. Liverpool and Rangers or Newcastle and Chelsea
3. 14
4. Liverpool, Chelsea and Cardiff
5. 15
6. 10
Owl Answers will vary, but should relate to the fact that teams will vary according to where children live.

page 47
Bar graphs

1.

Favourite films	Votes
Cinderella	40
Sleeping Beauty	60
Robin Hood	40
The Jungle Book	54
Beauty and the Beast	20
Snow White	66

2. Cinderella and Robin Hood
3. Snow White
4. Beauty and the Beast
5. 40
6. 40
Owl Answers will vary.

page 48
Bar graphs

1–5. Answers will vary depending on the book chosen.
Owl A survey of name lengths would show a greater frequency of word lengths of 3 letters and above, and very few 1- or 2-letter words.

Block D2

page 49
Adding and subtracting multiples of 10

1. $80 + 50 = 130\,cm$
2. $63 + 40 = 103\,cm$
3. $48 + 40 = 88\,cm$
4. $92 + 80 = 172\,cm$
5. $75 + 30 = 105\,cm$
6. $56 + 50 = 106\,cm$
7. $86 - 50 = 36$
8. $75 - 20 = 55$
9. $92 - 30 = 62$

page 49 continued

10. $66 - 40 = 26$
11. $85 - 60 = 25$
12. $71 - 50 = 21$
13. $36 - 10 = 26$
14. $47 - 20 = 27$
15. $78 - 40 = 38$
16. $55 - 40 = 15$
Owl $86 - 20 = 66$, $82 - 60 = 22$
$80 - 62 = 18$, $80 - 26 = 54$
$68 - 20 = 48$, $60 - 28 = 32$

page 50
Adding and subtracting multiples of I0

1. $126 + 40 = 166$
2. $148 + 30 = 178$
3. $87 + 30 = 117$
4. $117 + 30 = 147$
5. $139 + 50 = 189$
6. $447 + 30 = 477$
7. $331 \, g$
8. $715 \, g$
9. $462 \, g$
Owl Answers will vary.

page 5I
Adding and subtracting multiples of I0

1. $446 + 50 = 496 \, km/h$
2. $787 + 50 = 837 \, km/h$
3. $367 + 30 = 397 \, km/h$
4. $472 + 40 = 512 \, km/h$
5. $685 + 50 = 735 \, km/h$
6. $856 + 60 = 916 \, km/h$
7. $779 + 40 = 819 \, km/h$
8. $566 + 60 = 626 \, km/h$
9. $832 - 50 = 782 \, m$
10. $714 - 60 = 654 \, m$
11. $653 - 60 = 593 \, m$
12. $524 - 70 = 454 \, m$
13. $333 - 60 = 273 \, m$

14. $426 - 40 = 386 \, m$
15. $505 - 50 = 455 \, m$
16. $843 - 60 = 783 \, m$
Owl 12 and a half seconds

page 52
Adding and subtracting multiples of I0

1. $545 - 50 = 495$
2. $127 - 40 = 87$
3. $388 + 40 = 428$
4. $447 + 60 = 507$
5. $254 - 70 = 184$
6. $652 + 70 = 722$
7. £1·48 + 70p = £2·18
8. £2·86 + 40p = £3·26
9. £4·64 + 50p = £5·14
10. £3·71 + 60p = £4·31
11. £1·59 + 70p = £2·29
12. £2·95 + 20p = £3·15
13. 40, 30, 20 and either 5 and 1 or 4 and 2
The fewest throws she could have made is 4.

page 53
Adding

1. $64 + 21 = 85$
2. $72 + 26 = 98$
3. $47 + 32 = 79$
4. $54 + 31 = 85$
5. $68 + 21 = 89$
6. $57 + 22 = 79$
7. $45 + 41 = 86$
8. $38 + 22 = 60$
9. 55p + 26p = 81p
10. 63p + 27p = 90p
11. 48p + 53p = 101p or £1·01
12. 39p + 42p = 81p
13. 56p + 46p = 102p or £1·02
14. 45p + 28p = 73p
Owl Answers will vary.

page 54

Adding and subtracting

1. 85p − 22p = 63p
2. 64p − 22p = 42p
3. 88p − 15p = 73p
4. 95p − 34p = 61p
5. 77p − 33p = 44p
6. 53p − 23p = 30p
Owl Answers will vary.
7. £46 + £25 = £71
8. £58 + £135 = £193
9. £127 + £45 = £172
10. £116 + £56 = £172
11. £24 + £39 = £63
12. £66 + £55 = £121

page 55

Adding and subtracting

1. 328 + 48 = 376 g
2. 454 + 38 = 492 g
3. 562 + 39 = 601 g
4. 434 + 57 = 491 g
5. 669 + 28 = 697 g
6. 375 + 22 = 397 g
7. The answer is always a multiple of 9.
8. 374 − 23 = 351 km
9. 278 − 42 = 236 km
10. 165 − 33 = 132 km
11. 585 − 44 = 541 km
12. 294 − 52 = 242 km
13. 245 − 34 = 211 km

page 56

Adding and subtracting

1. £2·76 + 18p = £2·94
2. £3·25 + 28p = £3·53
3. £1·75 + 32p = £2·07
4. £2·60 + 15p = £2·75
5. £3·85 + 18p = £4·03
6. £2·80 + 15p = £2·95

7. Corrections:
   (b) 84 − 53 = 31
   (d) 254 − 42 = 212
   (e) 87 − 38 = 49
   (h) 74 − 35 = 39
   (j) 65 − 18 = 47
   5 out of 10 correct
Owl Answers will vary.

page 57

Adding and subtracting

1. 274 + 40 = 314 m
2. 364 + 50 = 414 m
3. 482 + 20 = 502 m
4. 275 + 50 = 325 m
5. 355 + 40 = 395 m
6. 568 + 30 = 598 m
7. 284 − 40 = 244 m
8. 361 − 30 = 331 m
9. 568 − 50 = 518 m
10. 486 − 60 = 426 m
11. 377 − 40 = 337 m
12. 295 − 50 = 245 m
Owl Any depth between 250 m and 300 m

page 58

Adding and subtracting

1. 224 − 40 = 184
2. 332 − 60 = 272
3. 512 − 30 = 482
4. 7 weeks
5. Pooja is 7 years old (+ 22 weeks) and her brother is 6 (+ 24 weeks).
6. 1400 + 300 = 1700
7. 2500 + 400 = 2900
8. 3100 + 700 = 3800
9. 6200 + 400 = 6600
10. 1500 + 200 = 1700
11. 2200 + 700 = 2900
12. 4300 + 300 = 4600
13. 5500 + 400 = 5900
14. 3400 + 200 = 3600
Owl Answers will vary.

page 59
Adding and subtracting

1. 8400 – 300 = 8100 m
2. 7800 – 400 = 7400 m
3. 7500 – 500 = 7000 m
4. 6900 – 500 = 6400 m
5. 6400 – 200 = 6200 m
6. 5800 – 300 = 5500 m
7. £2700 + £500 = £3200
8. £4500 + £600 = £5100
9. £3600 + £800 = £4400
10. £5800 + £500 = £6300

Owl Answers will vary. There are numerous possible ways for the Owl to get to the ground.

page 60
Adding and subtracting

1. 2600 – 800 = 1800
2. 4100 – 500 = 3600
3. 5600 – 900 = 4700
4. 3300 – 600 = 2700
5. 1500 – 700 = 800
6. 2400 – 800 = 1600

500 people were late:
1. 2600 + 500 = 3100
2. 4100 + 500 = 4600
3. 5600 + 500 = 6100
4. 3300 + 500 = 3800
5. 1500 + 500 = 2000
6. 2400 + 500 = 2900
7. 23 800 + 500 = 24 300
8. 16 200 + 800 = 17 000
9. 38 800 + 500 = 39 300
10. 35 700 + 700 = 36 400
11. 14 500 + 700 = 15 200
12. 67 400 + 800 = 68 200
13. 26 500 + 800 = 27 300
14. 46 800 + 800 = 47 600
15. 54 400 + 700 = 55 100

Owl Answers will vary.

page 61
Adding and subtracting

1. 49 + 6 = 55
2. 27 + 9 = 36
3. 38 + 9 = 47
4. 65 + 9 = 74
5. 73 + 9 = 82
6. 46 + 9 = 55
7. 27 + 11 = 38
8. 43 + 11 = 54
9. 28 + 11 = 39
10. 78p – 9p = 69p
11. 65p – 9p = 56p
12. 87p – 9p = 78p
13. 56p – 9p = 47p
14. 42p – 9p = 33p
15. 64p – 9p = 55p
16. 92p – 9p = 83p
17. 85p – 9p = 76p
18. 54p – 9p = 45p
19. 43p – 9p = 34p

Each price is reduced by 11p:
10. 78p – 11p = 67p
11. 65p – 11p = 54p
12. 87p – 11p = 76p
13. 56p – 11p = 45p
14. 42p – 11p = 31p
15. 64p – 11p = 53p
16. 92p – 11p = 81p
17. 85p – 11p = 74p
18. 54p – 11p = 43p
19. 43p – 11p = 32p

Owl 11 times

page 62
Adding and subtracting

1. 224 + 29 = 253
2. 342 + 19 = 361
3. 148 + 29 = 177
4. 563 + 21 = 584
5. 236 + 19 = 255
6. 472 + 21 = 493
7. False

8. True
9. True
10. £346 – £19 = £327
11. £542 – £19 = £523
12. £638 – £19 = £619
13. £456 – £21 = £435
14. £164 – £21 = £143
15. £288 – £31 = £257
Owl When you add 19 the units are 1 less than in the start number; when you subtract 19 the units are 1 more than in the start number.

page 63
Adding and subtracting

1. 354 + 39 = 393
2. 327 + 49 = 376
3. 312 + 29 = 341
4. 332 + 29 = 361
5. 325 + 59 = 384
6. 443 + 39 = 482
7. 250 – 29 = 221
    250 – 41 = 209
    250 – 99 = 151
    250 – 19 = 231
    250 – 39 = 211
    250 – 59 = 191
    250 – 119 = 131
    405 fish are not eaten altogether.
8. £582 – £39 = £543
9. £476 – £29 = £447
10. £553 – £31 = £522
11. £397 – £51 = £346
Owl 16 times, with 56 left

page 64
Adding and subtracting

1. 475 + 49 = 524
2. 268 + 49 = 317
3. 382 + 41 = 423
4. 550 + 59 = 609
5. 281 + 69 = 350
6. 198 + 59 = 257

7. 376 + 51 = 427
8. 498 + 41 = 539
9. 512 – 49 = 463
10. 642 – 59 = 583
11. 337 – 41 = 296
12. 424 – 51 = 373
13. 532 – 49 = 483
14. 618 – 39 = 579
15. 323 – 41 = 282
16. 415 – 59 = 356
Owl Answers will vary.

Block E2

page 65
Fives and tens

1. $3 \times 10 = 30$
2. $5 \times 10 = 50$
3. $4 \times 10 = 40$
4. $7 \times 10 = 70$
5. $10 \times 10 = 100$
6. $6 \times 10 = 60$
7. $9 \times 10 = 90$
Owl Answers will vary.
8. $5 \times 5 = 25$
9. $2 \times 5 = 10$
10. $6 \times 5 = 30$
11. $3 \times 5 = 15$
12. $10 \times 5 = 50$
13. $7 \times 5 = 35$
14. $8 \times 5 = 40$
15. $4 \times 5 = 20$
16. $9 \times 5 = 45$

page 66
Fives and tens

1. $3 \times 5p = 15p$
2. $5 \times 10p = 50p$
3. $5 \times 5p = 25p$
4. $7 \times 10p = 70p$
5. $4 \times 10p = 40p$
6. $6 \times 5p = 30p$

page 66 continued

7. $8 \times 5p = 40p$
8. $6 \times 10p = 60p$

Owl

1. 85p
2. 50p
3. 75p
4. 30p
5. 60p
6. 70p
7. 60p
8. 40p
9. 15
10. 30
11. 10
12. 45
13. 35
14. 20
15. 25
16. 40

page 67

Fives and tens

1. $4 \times 5p = 20p$
2. $2 \times 5p = 10p$
3. $7 \times 5p = 35p$
4. $10 \times 5p = 50p$
5. $20 \times 5p = 100p$ or £1
6. $6 \times 5p = 30p$

Owl 1p = 0 throws
2p = 0 throws
5p = 1 throw
10p = 2 throws
20p = 4 throws
£1 = 20 throws
£2 = 40 throws

7. $4 \times 5 = 20$
8. $6 \times 10 = 60$
9. $7 \times 5 = 35$
10. $4 \times 10 = 40$
11. $6 \times 5 = 30$
12. $8 \times 5 = 40$
13. $7 \times 10 = 70$

14. $9 \times 10 = 90$
15. $7 \times 5 = 35$
16. $12 \times 5 = 60$
17. $21 \times 5 = 105$
18. $32 \times 5 = 160$
19. $46 \times 5 = 230$
20. $14 \times 5 = 70$

page 68

Fives and tens

1. $35 \div 5 = 7, 5 \times 7 = 35$
2. $80 \div 10 = 8, 10 \times 8 = 80$
3. $40 \div 5 = 8, 5 \times 8 = 40$
4. $60 \div 10 = 6, 10 \times 6 = 60$
5. $25 \div 5 = 5, 5 \times 5 = 25$
6. $70 \div 10 = 7, 10 \times 7 = 70$
7. $15 \div 5 = 3, 5 \times 3 = 15$
8. $40 \div 10 = 4, 10 \times 4 = 40$
9. $45 \div 5 = 9, 5 \times 9 = 45$
10. 8 coins
11. 9 teams
12. 9 cars
13. $60 \div 5 = 12$
14. $90 \div 5 = 18$
15. $70 \div 5 = 14$
16. $160 \div 5 = 32$
17. $120 \div 5 = 24$
18. $230 \div 5 = 46$

page 69

Multiplying

1. a and d, b and h, c and f, e and g, i and j

Owl Children should draw rectangles representing: $1 \times 12, 12 \times 1$, $2 \times 6, 6 \times 2, 3 \times 4, 4 \times 3$.

2. $2 \times 4 = 8$
3. $5 \times 3 = 15$
4. $2 \times 8 = 16$
5. $6 \times 4 = 24$
6. $3 \times 7 = 21$
7. $9 \times 2 = 18$
8. $3 \times 6 = 18$

9. $4 \times 5 = 20$
10. $7 \times 6 = 42$

page 70
Multiplying

1. $2 \times 4 = 8, 4 \times 2 = 8$
2. $4 \times 3 = 12, 3 \times 4 = 12$
3. $3 \times 5 = 15, 5 \times 3 = 15$
4. $6 \times 2 = 12, 2 \times 6 = 12$
5. $2 \times 5 = 10, 5 \times 2 = 10$
6. $4 \times 6 = 24, 6 \times 4 = 24$
7. $6 \times 3 = 18, 3 \times 6 = 18$
8. $5 \times 4 = 20, 4 \times 5 = 20$
9. $3 \times 3 = 9$
10. $4 \times 2 = 8$
11. $5 \times 5 = 25$
12. $5 \times 2 = 10$
13. $3 \times 5 = 15$
14. $4 \times 3 = 12$
Owl Children should draw rectangles
   representing: $3 \times 4, 4 \times 3, 4 \times 4,$
   $2 \times 5, 5 \times 2, 3 \times 5, 5 \times 3, 4 \times 5,$
   $5 \times 4, 2 \times 6, 6 \times 2, 3 \times 6, 6 \times 3.$

page 7I
Multiplying and dividing

1. $12 \div 3 = 4$
2. $8 \div 4 = 2$
3. $15 \div 5 = 3$
4. $20 \div 4 = 5$
5. $18 \div 3 = 6$
6. $16 \div 8 = 2$
Multiplications for each set:
1. $3 \times 4 = 12, 4 \times 3 = 12$
2. $4 \times 2 = 8, 2 \times 4 = 8$
3. $5 \times 3 = 15, 3 \times 5 = 15$
4. $4 \times 5 = 20, 5 \times 4 = 20$
5. $3 \times 6 = 18, 6 \times 3 = 18$
6. $8 \times 2 = 16, 2 \times 8 = 16$
7. $3 \times 5 = 15, 15 \div 3 = 5, 15 \div 5 = 3$
8. $4 \times 6 = 24, 24 \div 4 = 6, 24 \div 6 = 4$
9. $5 \times 7 = 35, 35 \div 5 = 7, 35 \div 7 = 5$
10. $2 \times 8 = 16, 16 \div 8 = 2, 16 \div 2 = 8$

11. $6 \times 3 = 18, 18 \div 6 = 3, 18 \div 3 = 6$
12. $10 \times 4 = 40, 40 \div 10 = 4, 40 \div 4 = 10$
13. $8 \times 5 = 40, 40 \div 8 = 5, 40 \div 5 = 8$
14. $5 \times 4 = 20, 20 \div 5 = 4, 20 \div 4 = 5$
15. $9 \times 10 = 90, 90 \div 9 = 10, 90 \div 10 = 9$
Owl $2 \times 3 = 6, 3 \times 2 = 6$
   $6 \div 2 = 3, 6 \div 3 = 2$
   $3 \times 4 = 12, 4 \times 3 = 12$
   $12 \div 3 = 4, 12 \div 4 = 3$
   $2 \times 6 = 12, 6 \times 2 = 12$
   $12 \div 2 = 6, 12 \div 6 = 2$

page 72
Multiplying and dividing

1.

×	1	2	3	4	5	6
1	1	2	3	4	5	6
2	2	4	6	8	10	12
3	3	6	9	12	15	18
4	4	8	12	16	20	24
5	5	10	15	20	25	30
6	6	12	18	24	30	36

2. Answers will vary.
3. True
4. True
5. $48 \div 4 = 12$
6. $24 \div 6 = 4$
7. $120 \div 8 = 15$
8. $96 \div 4 = 24$
9. $96 \div 12 = 8$
10. $120 \div 15 = 8$
11. $15 \times 8 = 120$
12. $24 \times 4 = 96$
13. $144 \div 6 = 24$

page 73
Threes

1. $4 \times 3 = 12$
2. $6 \times 3 = 18$

Textbook 2

page 73 continued

3. $3 \times 3 = 9$
4. $10 \times 3 = 30$
5. $8 \times 3 = 24$
6. $5 \times 3 = 15$
7. $9 \times 3 = 27$
8. $2 \times 3 = 6$
9. $7 \times 3 = 21$
10. $9 \div 3 = 3$
11. $15 \div 3 = 5$
12. $27 \div 3 = 9$
13. $6 \div 3 = 2$
14. $30 \div 3 = 10$
15. $21 \div 3 = 7$
16. $12 \div 3 = 4$
17. $24 \div 3 = 8$
18. $18 \div 3 = 6$
Owl 180

page 74
Threes and sixes

1. $5 \times 3 = 15$
2. $6 \times 3 = 18$
3. $2 \times 3 = 6$
4. $4 \times 3 = 12$
5. $9 \times 3 = 27$
6. $3 \times 3 = 9$
Owl Answers will vary

1	2	3	4	5	6
7	8	9	10	11	12
13	14	15	16	17	18
19	20	21	22	23	24
25	26	27	28	29	30
31	32	33	34	35	36
37	38	39	40	41	42
43	44	45	46	47	48
49	50	51	52	53	54
55	56	57	58	59	60

7. 24
8. 42
9. 12
10. 60
11. 30
12. 36
Owl 66, 72, 78, 84, 90, 96, 102, 108, 114, 120

page 75
Threes and sixes

1. $4 \times 3 = 12$
   $4 \times 6 = 24$
2. $5 \times 3 = 15$
   $5 \times 6 = 30$
3. $8 \times 3 = 24$
   $8 \times 6 = 48$
4. $6 \times 3 = 18$
   $6 \times 6 = 36$
5. $9 \times 3 = 27$
   $9 \times 6 = 54$
6. 18
7. 24
8. 6
9. 36
10. $6 \times 3 = 18$
    $4 \times 1 = 4$
    $18 + 4 = 22$ points
11. $8 \times 3 = 24$
    $3 \times 1 = 3$
    $24 + 3 = 27$ points
12. $9 \times 3 = 27$
    $5 \times 1 = 5$
    $27 + 5 = 32$ points
13. $4 \times 3 = 12$
    $6 \times 1 = 6$
    $12 + 6 = 18$ points
14. $7 \times 3 = 21$
    $4 \times 1 = 4$
    $21 + 4 = 25$ points
15. $3 \times 3 = 9$
    $2 \times 1 = 2$
    $9 + 2 = 11$ points

Owl

10. $6 \times 4 = 24$
    $4 \times 2 = 8$
    $24 + 8 = 32$ points
11. $8 \times 4 = 32$
    $3 \times 2 = 6$
    $32 + 6 = 38$ points
12. $9 \times 4 = 36$
    $5 \times 2 = 10$
    $36 + 10 = 46$ points
13. $4 \times 4 = 16$
    $6 \times 2 = 12$
    $16 + 12 = 28$ points
14. $7 \times 4 = 28$
    $4 \times 2 = 8$
    $28 + 8 = 36$ points
15. $3 \times 4 = 12$
    $2 \times 2 = 4$
    $12 + 4 = 16$ points

page 76
Threes and sixes

1. $6 \div 3 = 2$
2. $15 \div 3 = 5$
3. $18 \div 6 = 3$
4. $24 \div 6 = 4$
5. $30 \div 6 = 5$
6. $21 \div 3 = 7$
7. $42 \div 6 = 7$
8. $18 \div 3 = 6$
9. $48 \div 6 = 8$
10. $27 \div 3 = 9$
11. 9 weeks
12. 8 teams, 1 child left over
13. 150
14. 180
15. 360
16. 240
17. $4 \times 60 = 240$
18. $6 \times 30 = 180$
19. $3 \times 30 = 90$
20. $9 \times 60 = 540$
21. $5 \times 60 = 300$
22. $7 \times 30 = 210$

page 77
Fractions

1. $\frac{1}{4}$
2. $\frac{3}{4}$
3. $\frac{4}{4}$
4. $\frac{2}{4}$
5. $\frac{2}{5}$
6. $\frac{5}{5}$
7. $\frac{4}{5}$
8. $\frac{1}{5}$
9. $\frac{3}{8}$
10. $\frac{5}{8}$
11. $\frac{1}{8}$
12. $\frac{7}{8}$
13. $\frac{3}{4}$
14. $\frac{5}{6}$
15. $\frac{3}{4}$
16. $\frac{2}{5}$
17. $\frac{4}{5}$
18. $\frac{2}{6}$ or $\frac{1}{3}$
19. $\frac{2}{4}$ or $\frac{1}{2}$
20. $\frac{4}{9}$
21. $\frac{7}{10}$

Owl

It is not possible to draw a rectangle to show $\frac{13}{25}$.

page 78
Fractions

1. $\frac{1}{6}$

page 78 continued

2. $\frac{1}{4}$

3. $\frac{3}{8}$

4. $\frac{4}{9}$

5. $\frac{3}{5}$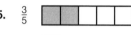

6. $\frac{1}{3}$

7. $\frac{3}{10}$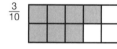

8. $\frac{3}{6}$

9. $\frac{5}{8}$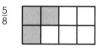

Owl Answers will vary.

10. $\frac{4}{8}$ or $\frac{1}{2}$

11. $\frac{4}{8}$ or $\frac{1}{2}$

12. $\frac{3}{8}$

13. $\frac{2}{8}$ or $\frac{1}{4}$

14. $\frac{7}{8}$

15. $\frac{4}{8}$ or $\frac{1}{2}$

16. $\frac{5}{8}$

17. $\frac{4}{8}$ or $\frac{1}{2}$

18. $\frac{4}{8}$ or $\frac{1}{2}$

page 79

Fractions

1. $\frac{1}{3}$ of 6 = 2
2. $\frac{2}{3}$ of 6 = 4
3. $\frac{3}{3}$ of 6 = 6
4. $\frac{1}{4}$ of 12 = 3
5. $\frac{2}{4}$ of 12 = 6
6. $\frac{3}{4}$ of 12 = 9
7. $\frac{1}{5}$ of 20 = 4
8. $\frac{3}{5}$ of 20 = 12
9. $\frac{4}{5}$ of 20 = 16
10. $\frac{3}{4}$ of 8 = 6
11. $\frac{2}{5}$ of 10 = 4
12. $\frac{7}{10}$ of 20 = 14
13. $\frac{3}{5}$ of 15 = 9
14. 10 girls
15. 2 matches
16. 6 plums

Owl Answers will vary.

page 80

Fractions

1. $\frac{2}{3}$ of 9 = 6
2. $\frac{1}{3}$ of 6 = 2
3. $\frac{2}{7}$ of 21 = 6
4. $\frac{3}{8}$ of 16 = 6
5. $\frac{5}{6}$ of 12 = 10
6. $\frac{2}{3}$ of 12 = 8
7. $\frac{1}{7}$ of 14 = 2
8. $\frac{3}{8}$ of 24 = 9
9. $\frac{7}{8}$ of 16 = 14
10. $\frac{2}{3}$ of 9
11. $\frac{3}{4}$ of 12
12. $\frac{5}{6}$ of 12
13. $\frac{4}{5}$ of 20
14. $\frac{5}{6}$ of 60

Owl You can find $\frac{2}{3}$ and $\frac{3}{4}$ of any number that is a multiple of both 3 and 4.

Textbook 2

Textbook 3

Block A3

page 3
Rounding to the nearest 10

1. $64 \rightarrow 60$
2. $72 \rightarrow 70$
3. $81 \rightarrow 80$
4. $46 \rightarrow 50$
5. $49 \rightarrow 50$
6. $53 \rightarrow 50$
7. $77 \rightarrow 80$
8. $84 \rightarrow 80$
9. $75 \rightarrow 80$
10. $45 \rightarrow 50$
11. $56 \rightarrow 60$
12. $61 \rightarrow 60$
13. $28p \rightarrow 30p$
14. $45p \rightarrow 50p$
15. $68p \rightarrow 70p$
16. $37p \rightarrow 40p$
17. $43p \rightarrow 40p$
18. $64p \rightarrow 60p$
Owl 95 to 104, 195 to 204

page 4
Nearest 10, nearest 100

1. $£125 \rightarrow £100$
2. $£248 \rightarrow £200$
3. $£569 \rightarrow £600$
4. $£750 \rightarrow £800$
5. $£933 \rightarrow £900$
6. $£487 \rightarrow £500$
7. $£275 \rightarrow £300$
8. $£360 \rightarrow £400$
Owl Answers will vary between 450 g and 500 g to 499 g and 549 g.
9. $468 \rightarrow 470$
10. $217 \rightarrow 220$
11. $652 \rightarrow 650$
12. $712 \rightarrow 710$

13. $902 \rightarrow 900$
14. $395 \rightarrow 400$
15. $555 \rightarrow 560$
16. $313 \rightarrow 310$

page 5
Nearest 10, nearest 100

1. $64p \rightarrow 60p$, $48p \rightarrow 50p$
   $60p + 50p = 110p = £1·10$
2. $57p \rightarrow 60p$, $34p \rightarrow 30p$
   $60p + 30p = 90p$
3. $78p \rightarrow 80p$, $27p \rightarrow 30p$
   $80p + 30p = 110p = £1·10$
Owl $64p + 48p + 57p + 34p + 78p + 27p$
   $= £3·08, £3·10$
   $60p + 50p + 60p + 30p + 80p + 30p$
   $= £3·10$
   The rounded totals are the same.
4. £9·50
5. 40 minutes
6. $348 \rightarrow 350, 300$
7. $212 \rightarrow 210, 200$
8. $641 \rightarrow 640, 600$
9. $772 \rightarrow 770, 800$
10. $453 \rightarrow 450, 500$
11. $584 \rightarrow 580, 600$
12. $633 \rightarrow 630, 600$
13. $536 \rightarrow 540, 500$

page 6
Nearest 10p, nearest £1

1. $£2·43 \rightarrow £2·40$
2. $£4·83 \rightarrow £4·80$
3. $£3·35 \rightarrow £3·40$
4. $£4·51 \rightarrow £4·50$
5. $£6·22 \rightarrow £6·20$
6. $£3·95 \rightarrow £4·00$
7. $£7·18 \rightarrow £7·20$
8. $£6·90 \rightarrow £6·90$
9. $£4·40 \rightarrow £4$

10. £3·15 → £3
11. £6·60 → £7
12. £5·50 → £6
13. £8·88 → £9
14. £6·06 → £6
15. £3·70 → £4
16. £8·65 → £9
17. £7·70 → £8
Owl Estimates will vary, the rounded amount comes to £56.

page 7
Adding and subtracting

1. £3·60 + 40p = £4
2. £2·80 + 20p = £3
3. £6·50 + 50p = £7
4. £1·10 + 90p = £2
5. £3·40 + 60p = £4
6. £5·70 + 30p = £6
7. £4·80 + 20p = £5
8. £3·60 + 40p = £4
9. £6·60 + 40p = £7
10. £3·20 + 80p = £4
11. £7·50 + 50p = £8
12. £5·70 + 30p = £6
Owl Sixteen amounts, between £1 and £1·50 to £2·50 and £3·00

page 8
Adding and subtracting

1. £2 – £1·30 = 70p
2. £3 – £2·70 = 30p
3. £2 – £1·90 = 10p
4. £4 – £3·20 = 80p
5. £3 – £2·40 = 60p
6. £5 – £4·60 = 40p
7. £6 – £5·40 = 60p
8. £5 – £4·20 = 80p
9. £10 – £9·30 = 70p
10. £8 – £7·80 = 20p
11. £7 – £6·50 = 50p
12. £5 – £4·10 = 90p
13. £6 – £5·60 = 40p

14. £8 – £7·20 = 80p
15. £7·20, 80p, £3·60
Owl Answers will vary.

page 9
Adding and subtracting

1. 100 – 60 = 40 cm
2. 110 – 90 = 20 cm
3. 200 – 196 = 4 cm
4. 150 – 139 = 11 cm
5. 130 – 70 = 60 cm
6. 220 – 190 = 30 cm
7. 360 + 680 = 1040
8. 420 – 80 = 340
9. 1330 – 570 = 760
10. 290 + 280 = 570
11. 420 – 340 = 80
12. 420 – 80 = 340
13. 1330 – 760 = 570
14. 1040 – 360 = 680
15. 3400 + 800 = 4200
Owl Answers will vary.

page 10
Adding and subtracting

1. £2·20 + £3·50 = £5·70
   £3·50 – £2·20 = £1·30
   £5·70 – £1·30 = £4·40
2. £1·20 + £2·60 = £3·80
   £2·60 – £1·20 = £1·40
   £3·80 – £1·40 = £2·40
3. £3·40 + £2·20 = £5·60
   £3·40 – £2·20 = £1·20
   £5·60 – £1·20 = £4·40
4. £1·20 + £2·50 = £3·70
   £2·50 – £1·20 = £1·30
   £3·70 – £1·30 = £2·40
5. £4·10 + £2·70 = £6·80
   £4·10 – £2·70 = £1·40
   £6·80 – £1·40 = £5·40
6. £3·20 + £2·40 = £5·60
   £3·20 – £2·40 = 80p
   £5·60 – 80p = £4·80

7. £2·80 + £1·10 = £3·90
   £2·80 − £1·10 = £1·70
   £3·90 − £1·70 = £2·20
8. £4·50 + £2·30 = £6·80
   £4·50 − £2·30 = £2·20
   £6·80 − £2·20 = £4·60
9. £2·70 + £4·10 = £6·80
   £4·10 − £2·70 = £1·40
   £6·80 − £1·40 = £5·40
10. The answer is double the lowest number.

page 11
Adding and subtracting

1. 10 + 82 = 92
2. 60 + 64 = 124
3. 40 + 57 = 97
4. 30 + 66 = 96
5. 70 + 78 = 148
6. 40 + 54 = 94
7. 46 + 70 = 116
8. 54 + 60 = 114
9. 82 + 50 = 132
10. 146 + 30 = 176
11. 173 + 20 = 193
12. 155 + 40 = 195
13. 261 + 30 = 291
14. 342 + 50 = 392
15. 437 + 50 = 487
Owl The great great great gran will be 100 years older than the grandchild.

page 12
Adding 2-digit numbers

1. 47 + 36 = 70 + 13 = 83
2. 52 + 48 = 90 + 10 = 100
3. 23 + 49 = 60 + 12 = 72
4. 78 + 17 = 80 + 15 = 95
5. 63 + 48 = 100 + 11 = 111
6. 36 + 27 = 50 + 13 = 63
7. 53 + 66 = 110 + 9 = 119
8. 45 + 74 = 110 + 9 = 119
9. 33 + 57 = 80 + 10 = 90

10. 48p + 67p = 115p
11. 74p + 65p = 139p
12. 81p + 49p = 130p
13. 56p + 72p = 128p
14. 47p + 63p = 110p
15. 63p + 59p = 122p
Owl 22 + 99, 33 + 88, 44 + 77, 55 + 66

page 13
Adding 2-digit numbers

1. 68 + 46 = 114
2. 174 + 17 = 191
3. 152 + 28 = 180
4. 317 + 74 = 391
5. 154 + 38 = 192
6. 128 + 63 = 191
7. 1837 + 64 = 1901
8. 1564 + 52 = 1616
9. 1491 + 56 = 1547
10. 1558 + 45 = 1603
11. 1820 + 90 = 1910
12. 1903 + 38 = 1941
Owl 40, 49, 58 or 67 years

page 14
Adding 2-digit numbers

1. 48 + 37 = 85 minutes, 8:25
2. 56 + 36 = 92 minutes, 10:32
3. 42 + 39 = 81 minutes, 11:21
4. 27 + 47 = 74 minutes, 9:14
Owl Pop Nation, Vet Rescue and News update
5. £1·64 + 28p = £1·92
6. £1·38 + 56p = £1·94
7. £1·29 + 49p = £1·78
8. £1·56 + 37p = £1·93
9. £1·62 + 33p = £1·95
10. £1·42 + 26p = £1·68

page 15
Doubling

1. double 5 → 10
2. double 6 → 12
3. double 7 → 14

page 15 continued

4. double 9 → 18
5. double 4 → 8
6. double 11 → 22
7. double 30p → 60p
8. double 50p → £1·00
9. double 60p → £1·20
10. double 40p → 80p
11. double 90p → £1·80
12. double 80p → £1·60
13. double 70p → £1·40
14. double 20p → 40p
15. Chang has 80p.
Owl It is better to start with 3p and double it six times.

page 16
Doubling, adding near doubles

1. double 13 = 26
2. double 17 = 34
3. double 15 = 30
4. double 12 = 24
5. double 14 = 28
6. double 19 = 38
7. True
8. True
9. False
10. False
11. double 13 = 26, 13 + 14 = 27
12. double 17 = 34, 17 + 18 = 35
13. double 15 = 30, 15 + 16 = 31
14. double 12 = 24, 12 + 11 = 23
15. double 9 = 18, 9 + 8 = 17
16. double 24 = 48, 24 + 25 = 49
17. double 19 = 38, 19 + 18 = 37
18. double 21 = 42, 21 + 22 = 43
Owl True
If you add numbers with a difference of 2, the answer is always even.

page 17
Doubling, adding near doubles

1. double 35p = 70p
2. double 65p = 130p or £1·30
3. double 85p = 170p or £1·70
4. double £1·35 = £2·70
5. double 70p = 140p or £1·40
6. double 15p = 30p
7. double 95p = 190p or £1·90
8. double 25p = 50p
9. 71p
10. 35 years
11. 1510 g
Owl Answers will vary.
12. double 35 = 70, 35 + 36 = 71
13. double 40 = 80, 40 + 41 = 81
14. double 25 = 50, 25 + 26 = 51
15. double 12 = 24, 12 + 13 = 25

page 18
Adding near doubles

1. 400 + 410 = 810 m
2. 350 + 360 = 710 m
3. 240 + 250 = 490 m
4. 750 + 760 = 1510 m
5. 600 + 610 = 1210 m
6. 260 + 250 = 510
7. 25 + 26 = 51
8. 45 + 46 = 91
9. 18 + 19 = 37, 28 + 29 = 57, 38 + 39 = 77, 48 + 49 = 97
Owl Answers will vary.
2 + 3 + 4 = 9, 3 + 4 + 5 = 12,
4 + 5 + 6 = 15, 5 + 6 + 7 = 18

Block B3

page 19
Counting in 2s, even and odd

1. 8, 10, 12
2. 21, 23, 25
3. 47, 49, 51
4. 38, 40, 42
5. 7, 9, 11
6. 20, 22, 24
7. 64 even

8. 27 odd
9. 31 odd
10. 45 odd
11. 54 even
12. 18 even
13. 9 odd
14. 11 odd
15. 14
16. 4, 6, 8 or 10
Owl Answers will vary. An example might be 53.

page 20
Counting in 5s and 50s

1. 25p, 30p
2. 40p, 45p
3. 45p, 50p
4. 85p, 90p
5. 70p, 75p
6. 75p, 80p
7. 55p, 60p
8. 35p, 40p
9. 350, 400, 450
10. 1150, 1200, 1250
11. 750, 800, 850
12. 400, 450, 500
13. 900, 950, 1000
14. 550, 600, 650

15. 450, 500, 550
16. 700, 750, 800
17. 850, 900, 950
Owl 20

page 21
Counting in 50s

1. 850, 900, 950
2. 650, 700, 750
3. 500, 550, 600
4. 750, 800, 850
5. 450, 500, 550, 600
6. 700, 750, 800, 850
7. 350, 400, 450, 500
8. 300, 350, 400, 450
9. True
10. False
11. False
12. True
13. 367 odd
14. 419 odd
15. 225 odd
16. 404 even
17. 607 odd
18. 111 odd
19. 912 even
20. 334 even
Owl 18, 36, 54, 72 or 90

page 22
Counting

1.

	600	705	750	1005	810	100	48	130	350	950	415
Even/odd	Even	Odd	Even	Odd	Even	Even	Even	Even	Even	Even	Odd
In 50s count	✓		✓			✓			✓	✓	
In 5s count	✓	✓	✓	✓	✓	✓		✓	✓	✓	✓

2. The pattern is that every alternate number increases by 1 each time.
3. 75, 100, 125
4. 225, 250, 275
5. 350, 375, 400
6. 150, 175, 200
7. 125, 150, 175
8. 275, 300, 325

page 22 continued

9. 14 weeks
10. 40 days

page 23

Fours

1	2	3	4
5	6	7	8
9	10	11	12
13	14	15	16
17	18	19	20
21	22	23	24
25	26	27	28
29	30	31	32
33	34	35	36
37	38	39	40

1. 8
2. 40
3. 20
4. 16
5. 12
6. 28
7. 24
8. 36
9. $3 \times 4 = 12$
10. $5 \times 4 = 20$
11. $2 \times 4 = 8$
12. $4 \times 4 = 16$
13. $10 \times 4 = 40$
14. $7 \times 4 = 28$
Owl Answers will vary.

page 24

Fours

1. $3 \times 2 = 6, 3 \times 4 = 12$
2. $5 \times 2 = 10, 5 \times 4 = 20$
3. $7 \times 2 = 14, 7 \times 4 = 28$
4. $4 \times 2 = 8, 4 \times 4 = 16$
5. $9 \times 2 = 18, 9 \times 4 = 36$

6. $6 \times 2 = 12, 6 \times 4 = 24$
7. $8 \times 2 = 16, 8 \times 4 = 32$
Owl Repeat the pattern used above, for example, $1 \times 4 = 4, 1 \times 8 = 8$; $2 \times 4 = 8, 2 \times 8 = 16$, and so on.
8. $5 \times 4 = 20$
9. $6 \times 4 = 24$
10. $2 \times 4 = 8$
11. $3 \times 4 = 12$
12. $10 \times 4 = 40$
13. $7 \times 4 = 28$
14. $4 \times 4 = 16$
15. $9 \times 4 = 36$
16. $6 \times 4 = 24$
17. $5 \times 4 = 20$
18. $8 \times 4 = 32$

page 25

Fours

1. 16
2. 24
3. $12 \div 4 = 3$
4. $20 \div 4 = 5$
5. $40 \div 4 = 10$
6. $4 \div 4 = 1$
7. $36 \div 4 = 9$
8. $28 \div 4 = 7$
9. $32 \div 4 = 8$
10. $24 \div 4 = 6$
11. $16 \div 4 = 4$
Owl 44, 48, 52, 56, 60, 64, 68, 72, 76
12. 24 season changes
13. 56 slices
14. 9 tables (2 chairs left over)

page 26

Fours

1. $12 \div 4 = 3$
2. $5 \times 4 = 20$
3. $40 \div 4 = 10$
4. $7 \times 4 = 28$
5. $32 \div 4 = 8$
6. $4 \div 4 = 1$

7. $6 \times 4 = 24$
8. $9 \times 4 = 36$
9. $28 \div 4 = 7$
10. True
11. True
12. True
13. 160
14. 280
15. $3 \times 40 = 120$
16. $5 \times 40 = 200$
17. $9 \times 40 = 360$
18. $6 \times 40 = 240$
19. $8 \times 40 = 320$
20. $7 \times 40 = 280$

page 27
Turning

1. less than
2. more than
3. equal to
4. equal to
5. more than
6. less than
7. 2 right angles
8. 1 right angle
9. 3 right angles
10. 1 right angle
11. 2 right angles
12. 4 right angles

Owl See below for the new position of the baton after it has turned through another 5 right angles.
1 right-angle turn will end up in the same position.

7.
8.
9.
10.

11.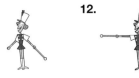
12.

page 28
Turning

1. Ghost Train
2. Wall of Death
3. Wall of Death
4. Wall of Death
5. Ghost Train
6. Big Dipper
7. Wall of Death
8. Ghost Train
   Rick: anticlockwise, 1 right angle
   Liz: clockwise, 3 right angles
   Kevi: anticlockwise, 2 right angles
   Pam: clockwise, 4 right angles

Owl Answers will vary.

page 29
Turning

1. 6
2. 3
3. 3
4. 9
5. 10
6. 1

Owl 3 right-angle turns in the opposite direction or 5 right-angle turns in the same direction

7. True
8. False
9. True
10. True

page 30
Turning

1. 2 right angles
2. 3 right angles
3. 1 right angle

page 30 continued

4. 3 right angles
5. $\frac{1}{3}$ right angle
6. 2 right angles
7. $1\frac{1}{3}$ right angles
8. $3\frac{1}{3}$ right angles

9–12. Answers will vary.

Owl Answers will vary.

page 31

North, South, East, West

1. West
2. East
3. South
4. East
5. South
6. North
7. West
8. South
   East, West, North, West, North, South, East, North

Owl Answers will vary.

page 32

North, South, East, West

1. East
2. South
3. West
4. West
5. East
6. South
7. East
8. North
9. West
10. East, South
11. West, North

Owl Answers will vary.

page 33

North, South, East, West

1.
2.

3. ⬠
4. ▭
5. ▷
6. ⬡
7. ▷ △
8. ◺
9. ◺
10. ▷
11. ☐
12. ◯
13. ◺

Owl Answers will vary.

page 34

North, South, East, West

1. East 2 km, North 2 km, East 2 km, South 5 km
2. West 3 km, South 2 km, East 2 km, North 4 km
3. West 4 km, North 2 km, East 2 km, South 4 km
4. East 5 km, North 3 km, West 3 km, South 4 km, East 4 km

Owl Answers will vary.

5. South
6. North
7. West
8. West
9. South
10. North

Block C3

page 35

Grams

1. 600 grams
2. 300 grams

3. 200 grams
4. 500 grams
5. 100 grams
6. 700 grams
Owl Lunch, pencil case and calculator
7. 1 kg 300 g
8. 700 g
9. 2 kg 900 g
10. 4 kg 600 g
11. 2 kg 300 g
12. 4 kg 400 g
13. 9 kg 600 g
14. 2 kg 400 g
15. 6 kg 800 g

page 36
Grams and kilograms

1. 1100 g
2. 2600 g
3. 3400 g
4. 1500 g
5. 2300 g
6. 4500 g
7. 1 kg 200 g
8. 3 kg 500 g
9. 1 kg 700 g
10. 1 kg 500 g
Owl 24, 70, 34, 30
11. 10
12. 2
13. 5
14. 20
15. 100
16. 4

page 37
Grams and kilograms

1. 20
2. 5 kg
3. 1 kg
4. 20
5. True
6. False

7. False
8. False
9. Answers will vary.

page 38
Position

1. C2
2. D4
3. E2
4. D1
5. B1
6. A4
7. D2
8. D3
9. A1
10. Mrs Sums
11. Mr Keen
12. Mrs Winnett
13. Flopsy
14. Mrs Cotter
15. Mrs Grim
Owl Answers will vary.

page 39
Position

1. A5
2. D1
3. E1
4. E3
5. D5
6. C5
7. A1
8. B1
9. sheep
10. house
11. goats
12. river
13. orchard
14. flowers
15. hedgehogs, goats, otters
16. sheep pen, barn, wheat, goats, orchard
Owl Answers will vary.

page 40
Position

1. (a) E3 (b) B5 (c) E1 (d) F5
   (e) A2 (f) C1 (g) C4 (h) D6

2.

3.

4.

page 41
Months of the year

1. January, February, March, April, May, June, July, August, September, October, November, December
2. March
3. September
4. November
5. April
6. May, June, July
7. August
8. June
9. January, February, March, April, September, October, November, December
10. September
11. February

Owl June or July

page 42
Days and weeks

1. 15 days
2. 24 days
3. 12 days
4. 36 days
5. 34 days
6. 50 days
7. 23 days
8. 22 days
9. 2 weeks 3 days
10. 2 weeks 6 days
11. 7 weeks 1 day
12. 3 weeks 4 days
13. 4 weeks 2 days
14. 14 weeks 2 days

Owl Answers will vary.

page 43
Days, weeks, months and years

1. 1 year 1 month
2. 1 year 6 months
3. 2 years 2 months
4. 3 years 3 months
5. 4 years 2 months
6. 10 years 0 months
7. 7 days
8. 12 months
9. 52 weeks
10. 24 months
11. 365 days
12. 100 years

Owl 12 000 months in a millennium, 52 000 weeks in a millennium

13. 1 day
14. 14th May

page 44
Calendars

1. Friday
2. Thursday

3. Tuesday
4. Sunday
5. Saturday
6. Saturday
7. Thursday
8. Friday
9. Tuesday
10. Tuesday
11. 11th
12. 15th
13. 27th
14. 5th
15. 30th
16. 24th
17. 11th
18. 5th
19. Answers will vary.

page 45
Venn diagrams

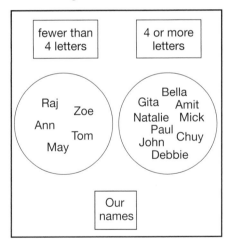

Answers will vary, depending on the words children add to the diagram. Possible words to add to the diagram include mix, maths, today.
Owl Answers will vary.

page 46
Carroll diagrams

	Joining word	Not joining word
Short word (fewer than 4 letters)	but and	cat dog
Long word (4 or more letters)	where because which	chair table

Owl Column = Electronic, Not electronic
Row = Small, Big

page 47
Carroll and Venn diagrams

	2 syllables or fewer	More than 2 syllables
Words rhyming with sea	tree free wispy bee	blustery cheerfully summary
Words not rhyming with sea	autumn sun wasp spring wind	beautiful imagining

Answers will vary. The information should be presented in a Venn diagram. Possible labels include: 2 syllables or fewer, words rhyming with sea.
Owl Answers will vary.

page 48
Carroll and Venn diagrams
Possible animals to add are in italics.

	Animals with fur/hair	Animals without fur/hair
Pets	rabbit gerbil *cat*	goldfish stick insect lizard *spider*
Not pets	kangaroo koala *lion*	*crocodile*

Textbook 3

	Multiples of 3	Not multiples of 3
Odd	21 27 33 39 45	23 25 29 31 35 37 41 43 47 49
Even	24 30 36 42 48	22 26 28 32 34 38 40 44 46

Owl Multiples of an even number would make the first region empty.

Block D3

page 49
Tens and units

1. $30 + 20 = 50$, $6 + 3 = 9$, $50 + 9 = 59$
2. $50 + 20 = 70$, $4 + 4 = 8$, $70 + 8 = 78$
3. $60 + 20 = 80$, $7 + 1 = 8$, $80 + 8 = 88$
4. $70 + 20 = 90$, $2 + 7 = 9$, $90 + 9 = 99$
5. $50 + 40 = 90$, $3 + 4 = 7$, $90 + 7 = 97$
6. $60 + 20 = 80$, $5 + 5 = 10$, $80 + 10 = 90$
7. $40 + 30 = 70$, $8 + 6 = 14$, $70 + 14 = 84$
8. $60 + 30 = 90$, $5 + 7 = 12$, $90 + 12 = 102$
9. $50 + 30 = 80$, $6 + 6 = 12$, $80 + 12 = 92$
10. $30 + 40 = 70$, $9 + 4 = 13$, $70 + 13 = 83$
11. $50 + 20 = 70$, $7 + 6 = 13$, $70 + 13 = 83$
12. $40 + 30 = 70$, $2 + 8 = 10$, $70 + 10 = 80$
13. £8

Owl Answers will vary.

page 50
Hundreds, tens and units

1. $36 + 47 + 54 = 30 + 40 + 50 = 120$, $6 + 7 + 4 = 17$, $120 + 17 = 137$ cm
2. $42 + 28 + 38 = 40 + 20 + 30 = 90$, $2 + 8 + 8 = 18$, $90 + 18 = 108$ cm
3. $53 + 27 + 41 = 50 + 20 + 40 = 110$, $3 + 7 + 1 = 11$, $110 + 11 = 121$ cm
4. $62 + 52 + 38 = 60 + 50 + 30 = 140$, $2 + 2 + 8 = 12$, $140 + 12 = 152$ cm

Owl $140 + 110 + 120 + 150 = 520$ cm, $137 + 108 + 121 + 152 = 518$ cm
There is a 2 cm difference.

5. £108
6. £139
7. $146 + 32 + 64$: $40 + 30 + 60 = 130$, $6 + 2 + 4 = 12$, $100 + 130 + 12 = 242$
8. $128 + 37 + 56$: $20 + 30 + 50 = 100$, $8 + 7 + 6 = 21$, $100 + 100 + 21 = 221$
9. $135 + 28 + 36$: $30 + 20 + 30 = 80$, $5 + 8 + 6 = 19$, $100 + 80 + 19 = 199$
10. $245 + 27 + 26$: $40 + 20 + 20 = 80$, $5 + 7 + 6 = 18$, $200 + 80 + 18 = 298$
11. $117 + 36 + 45$: $10 + 30 + 40 = 80$, $7 + 6 + 5 = 18$, $100 + 80 + 18 = 198$
12. $241 + 27 + 18$: $40 + 20 + 10 = 70$, $1 + 7 + 8 = 16$, $200 + 70 + 16 = 286$

page 51
Hundreds, tens and units

1. $100 + 80 + 17 = 197$ g
2. $100 + 80 + 21 = 201$ g
3. $100 + 110 + 17 = 227$ g
4. $100 + 120 + 17 = 237$ g
5. $100 + 120 + 12 = 232$ g
6. $100 + 140 + 17 = 257$ g
7. $761 + 52 + 43 = 855$
The total will be 1 less.
8. $£146 + £58 + £37 = £241$
9. $£128 + £64 + £32 = £224$
10. $£117 + £86 + £18 = £221$
11. $£127 + £54 + £31 = £212$

page 52
Hundreds, tens and units

1. $100 + 100 = 200$, $20 + 50 + 10 = 80$, $7 + 4 + 5 = 16$, $200 + 80 + 16 = 296$ kg

2. $100 + 100 = 200, 20 + 10 + 30 = 60,$
$4 + 6 = 10, 200 + 60 + 10 = 270\,kg$

3. $10 + 70 + 20 = 100, 2 + 3 + 3 = 8,$
$100 + 100 + 8 = 208\,kg$

4. $50 + 80 = 130, 5 + 7 + 5 = 17,$
$100 + 130 + 17 = 247\,kg$

Owl $12 + 345 + 6789 = 7146$
$98 + 765 + 4321 = 5184$

5. 301 miles

6. 228 days

Owl Answers will vary.

page 53
Adding

Children should also include estimates.

1.
```
  T U
  3 6
+ 2 3
----
  9
5 0
----
5 9
```

2.
```
  T U
  3 6
+ 4 2
----
  8
7 0
----
7 8
```

3.
```
  H T U
    2 8
+   9 1
-----
    9
1 1 0
-----
1 1 9
```

4.
```
  T U
  4 5
+ 3 4
----
  9
7 0
----
7 9
```

5.
```
  T U
  1 7
+ 4 2
----
  9
5 0
----
5 9
```

6.
```
  T U
  3 2
+ 1 2
----
  4
4 0
----
4 4
```

7.
```
  T U
  5 1
+ 2 5
----
  6
7 0
----
7 6
```

8.
```
  T U
  4 2
+ 3 3
----
  5
7 0
----
7 5
```

9. Answers will vary.

Owl $25 + 26 = 51$

page 54
Adding

Children should also include estimates.

1.
```
  H T U
    4 6
    2 8
+   7 3
-----
    1 7
1 3 0
-----
1 4 7
```

2.
```
  H T U
      6 8
      3 7
+     4 5
      2 0
    1 3 0
    1 5 0
```

3.
```
  H T U
      7 3
      8 1
+     2 4
        8
    1 7 0
    1 7 8
```

4.
```
    T U
    3 8
    1 4
+   3 2
    1 4
    7 0
    8 4
```

5.
```
  H T U
      5 6
      2 7
+     3 9
      2 2
    1 0 0
    1 2 2
```

6.
```
    T U
    4 8
    3 3
+   1 7
    1 8
    8 0
    9 8
```

7.
```
  H T U
      6 2
      3 7
+     2 6
      1 5
    1 1 0
    1 2 5
```

Textbook 3

8. Answers will vary.

Owl Rockets: 168 m and 135 m
Fuel pods: 43 m and 54 m

page 55
Adding
Children should also include estimates.

1.
```
H T U
2 4 7
+   3 8
2 8 5
```

2.
```
H T U
1 6 4
+   5 8
2 2 2
```

3.
```
H T U
3 8 2
+   6 4
4 4 6
```

4.
```
H T U
1 3 8
+   1 6
1 5 4
```

5.
```
H T U
1 4 6
+   3 7
1 8 3
```

6.
```
H T U
1 2 8
+   3 1
1 5 9
```

7.
```
H T U
4 6 3
+   6 9
5 3 2
```

8. 437 stamps
9. £622 000
10. 240 miles
Owl Answers will vary.

page 56
Adding

Children should also include estimates.

1.
```
  H T U
  3 7 4
+ 2 6 8
  6 4 2
```

2.
```
  H T U
  2 8 6
+ 4 1 8
  7 0 4
```

3.
```
  H T U
  3 7 5
+ 1 8 8
  5 6 3
```

4.
```
  H T U
  2 7 8
+ 1 8 7
  4 6 5
```

5.
```
  H T U
  3 9 2
+ 1 2 9
  5 2 1
```

6.
```
  H T U
  1 8 8
+ 2 7 6
  4 6 4
```

7.
```
  H T U
  2 8 3
+ 3 7 9
  6 6 2
```

8. $294 + 516 = 810$
9. 2001
10. 1999

page 57
Difference

1. $2 + 10 + 1 = 13$
2. $3 + 20 + 2 = 25$
3. $2 + 30 + 5 = 37$
4. $5 + 10 + 2 = 17$
5. $4 + 10 + 3 = 17$
6. $6 + 10 + 1 = 17$
7. $4p + 10p + 4p = 18p$
8. $5p + 2p = 7p$
9. $3p + 1p = 4p$
10. $5p + 10p + 3p = 18p$
11. $2p + 10p + 2p = 14p$
12. $7p + 10p + 8p = 25p$
13. 17p
14. 19 years

Owl Answers will vary.

page 58
Difference

1. $3 + 10 + 5 = 18$
2. $6 + 30 + 2 = 38$
3. $6 + 30 + 5 = 41$
4. $9 + 30 = 39$
5. $3 + 40 + 8 = 51$
6. $8 + 10 + 12 = 30\,cm$
7. $3 + 30 + 2 = 35\,cm$
8. $2 + 20 + 11 = 33\,cm$
9. $4 + 40 + 39 = 83\,cm$
10. $2 + 100 + 7 = 109\,cm$
11. $7 + 50 + 9 = 66\,cm$
12. $9 + 150 + 8 = 167\,cm$
13. $6 + 70 + 2 = 78\,cm$

Owl Possible answers will fall between
9·72 m (4·71 m & 5·01 m) and
10·28 m (4·99 m & 5·29 m).

page 59
Difference

1. $2 + 30 + 16 = 48$
   difference = £48
2. $2 + 10 + 2 = 14$
   difference = £14

Textbook 3

page 59 continued

3. $6 + 40 + 8 = 54$
   difference = £54
4. $7 + 10 + 18 = 35$
   difference = £35

Owl £475 and £525

5. 62 m
6. 65 m
7. $3p + 30p = 33p$
8. $4p + 30p + £1 = £1·34$
9. $9p + 10p + £2 = £2·19$
10. $2p + 40p = 42p$
11. $3p + 10p + £2 = £2·13$

page 60

Difference

1. $8 + 20 + 100 + 12 = 140$
2. $6 + 30 + 100 + 21 = 157$
3. $5 + 20 + 100 + 13 = 138$
4. $8 + 30 + 100 + 11 = 149$
5. $4 + 70 + 100 + 42 = 216$
6. $5 + 30 + 100 + 32 = 167$

Owl The difference is 91.

7. 49
8. 479
9. 359
10. 203
11. Answers will vary. An example might be 32 and 64.
12. 376

page 61

Subtraction

1.
$$\begin{array}{r} 64 \\ -\ 30 \\ \hline \end{array} = \begin{array}{r} 60 + 4 \\ -\ 30 \\ \hline 30 + 4 = 34 \end{array}$$

2.
$$\begin{array}{r} 78 \\ -\ 22 \\ \hline \end{array} = \begin{array}{r} 70 + 8 \\ -\ 20 + 2 \\ \hline 50 + 6 = 56 \end{array}$$

3.
$$\begin{array}{r} 86 \\ -\ 12 \\ \hline \end{array} = \begin{array}{r} 80 + 6 \\ -\ 10 + 2 \\ \hline 70 + 4 = 74 \end{array}$$

4.
$$\begin{array}{r} 76 \\ -\ 20 \\ \hline \end{array} = \begin{array}{r} 70 + 6 \\ -\ 20 \\ \hline 50 + 6 = 56 \end{array}$$

5.
$$\begin{array}{r} 69 \\ -\ 34 \\ \hline \end{array} = \begin{array}{r} 60 + 9 \\ -\ 30 + 4 \\ \hline 30 + 5 = 35 \end{array}$$

6.
$$\begin{array}{r} 88 \\ -\ 40 \\ \hline \end{array} = \begin{array}{r} 80 + 8 \\ -\ 40 \\ \hline 40 + 8 = 48 \end{array}$$

7.
$$\begin{array}{r} 84 \\ -\ 22 \\ \hline \end{array} = \begin{array}{r} 80 + 4 \\ -\ 20 + 2 \\ \hline 60 + 2 = 62\,\text{cm} \end{array}$$

8.
$$\begin{array}{r} 68 \\ -\ 22 \\ \hline \end{array} = \begin{array}{r} 60 + 8 \\ -\ 20 + 2 \\ \hline 40 + 6 = 46\,\text{cm} \end{array}$$

9.
$$\begin{array}{r} 95 \\ -\ 22 \\ \hline \end{array} = \begin{array}{r} 90 + 5 \\ -\ 20 + 2 \\ \hline 70 + 3 = 73\,\text{cm} \end{array}$$

10.
$$\begin{array}{r} 56 \\ -\ 22 \\ \hline \end{array} = \begin{array}{r} 50 + 6 \\ -\ 20 + 2 \\ \hline 30 + 4 = 34\,\text{cm} \end{array}$$

11.
$$\begin{array}{r} 65 \\ -\ 22 \\ \hline \end{array} = \begin{array}{r} 60 + 5 \\ -\ 20 + 2 \\ \hline 40 + 3 = 43\,\text{cm} \end{array}$$

12.
$$\begin{array}{r} 79 \\ -\ 22 \\ \hline \end{array} = \begin{array}{r} 70 + 9 \\ -\ 20 + 2 \\ \hline 50 + 7 = 57\,\text{cm} \end{array}$$

Owl 40 cm, 24 cm, 51 cm, 12 cm, 21 cm, 35 cm

page 62

Subtraction

1.
$$\begin{array}{r} 88 \\ -\ 23 \\ \hline \end{array} = \begin{array}{r} 80 + 8 \\ -\ 20 + 3 \\ \hline 60 + 5 = 65\,\text{cm} \end{array}$$

2. $94 = 90 + 4$
　　$- 42 \quad - 40 + 2$
　　$\overline{} \quad \overline{50 + 2} = 52\,cm$

3. $68 = 60 + 8$
　　$- 45 \quad - 40 + 5$
　　$\overline{} \quad \overline{20 + 3} = 23\,cm$

4. $78 = 70 + 8$
　　$- 32 \quad - 30 + 2$
　　$\overline{} \quad \overline{40 + 6} = 46\,cm$

5. $67 = 60 + 7$
　　$- 44 \quad - 40 + 4$
　　$\overline{} \quad \overline{20 + 3} = 23\,cm$

6. $93 = 90 + 3$
　　$- 13 \quad - 10 + 3$
　　$\overline{} \quad \overline{80 + 0} = 80\,cm$

Owl 3 days

7. $43 = 30 + 13$
　　$- 28 \quad - 20 + 8$
　　$\overline{} \quad \overline{10 + 5} = 15\,cm$

8. $68 = 60 + 8$
　　$- 31 \quad - 30 + 1$
　　$\overline{} \quad \overline{30 + 7} = 37\,cm$

9. $95 = 90 + 5$
　　$- 42 \quad - 40 + 2$
　　$\overline{} \quad \overline{50 + 3} = 53\,cm$

10. $28 = 20 + 8$
　　$- 12 \quad - 10 + 2$
　　$\overline{} \quad \overline{10 + 6} = 16\,cm$

page 63
Subtraction

1. $54 = 40 + 14$
　　$- 37 \quad - 30 + 7$
　　$\overline{} \quad \overline{10 + 7} = 17\,p$

2. $68 = 50 + 18$
　　$- 49 \quad - 40 + 9$
　　$\overline{} \quad \overline{10 + 9} = 19\,p$

3. $43 = 30 + 13$
　　$- 27 \quad - 20 + 7$
　　$\overline{} \quad \overline{10 + 6} = 16\,p$

4. $72 = 60 + 13$
　　$- 38 \quad - 30 + 8$
　　$\overline{} \quad \overline{30 + 4} = 34\,p$

5. $54 = 40 + 14$
　　$- 26 \quad - 20 + 6$
　　$\overline{} \quad \overline{20 + 8} = 28\,p$

6. $65 = 50 + 15$
　　$- 17 \quad - 10 + 7$
　　$\overline{} \quad \overline{40 + 8} = 48\,p$

7. Answers will vary.
8. 26 years old
9. £28

page 64
Subtraction

1. 362
　　$- \ \ 48$
　　$\overline{}$

$$= 300 + 60 + 2 = 300 + 50 + 12$$
$$- 40 + 8 \quad \underline{- 40 + \ 8}$$
$$\overline{300 + 10 + \ 4} = 314\,m$$

2. 453
　　$- \ \ 39$
　　$\overline{}$

$$= 400 + 50 + 3 = 400 + 40 + 13$$
$$- 30 + 9 \quad \underline{- 30 + \ 9}$$
$$\overline{400 + 10 + \ 4} = 414\,m$$

3. 522
　　$- \ \ 18$
　　$\overline{}$

$$= 500 + 20 + 2 = 500 + 10 + 12$$
$$- 10 + 8 \quad \underline{- 10 + \ 8}$$
$$\overline{500 + \ 0 + \ 4} = 504\,m$$

4. 384
$-$ 67
___

$= 300 + 80 + 4 = 300 + 70 + 14$
$\quad\quad - 60 + 7 \quad\quad\quad - 60 + 7$
$\quad\quad\quad\quad\quad\quad \overline{300 + 10 + 7} = 317\,\text{m}$

5. 452
$-$ 29
___

$= 400 + 50 + 2 = 400 + 40 + 12$
$\quad\quad - 20 + 9 \quad\quad\quad - 20 + 9$
$\quad\quad\quad\quad\quad\quad \overline{400 + 20 + 3} = 423\,\text{m}$

6. 493
$-$ 56
___

$= 400 + 90 + 3 = 400 + 80 + 13$
$\quad\quad - 50 + 6 \quad\quad\quad - 50 + 6$
$\quad\quad\quad\quad\quad\quad \overline{400 + 30 + 7} = 437\,\text{m}$

7. 468
$-$ 19
___

$= 400 + 60 + 8 = 400 + 50 + 18$
$\quad\quad - 10 + 9 \quad\quad\quad - 10 + 9$
$\quad\quad\quad\quad\quad\quad \overline{400 + 40 + 9} = 449$

8. 544
$-$ 29
___

$= 500 + 40 + 4 = 500 + 30 + 14$
$\quad\quad - 20 + 9 \quad\quad\quad - 20 + 9$
$\quad\quad\quad\quad\quad\quad \overline{500 + 10 + 5} = 515$

9. 372
$-$ 38
___

$= 300 + 70 + 2 = 300 + 60 + 12$
$\quad\quad - 30 + 8 \quad\quad\quad - 30 + 8$
$\quad\quad\quad\quad\quad\quad \overline{300 + 30 + 4} = 334$

10. 494
$-$ 68
___

$= 400 + 90 + 4 = 400 + 80 + 14$
$\quad\quad - 60 + 8 \quad\quad\quad - 60 + 8$
$\quad\quad\quad\quad\quad\quad \overline{400 + 20 + 6} = 426$

11. 567
$-$ 29
___

$= 500 + 60 + 7 = 500 + 50 + 17$
$\quad\quad - 20 + 9 \quad\quad\quad - 20 + 9$
$\quad\quad\quad\quad\quad\quad \overline{500 + 30 + 8} = 538$

12. 482
$-$ 37
___

$= 400 + 80 + 2 = 400 + 70 + 12$
$\quad\quad - 30 + 7 \quad\quad\quad - 30 + 7$
$\quad\quad\quad\quad\quad\quad \overline{400 + 40 + 5} = 445$

Owl Answers will vary.

Block E3

page 65

Dividing

1. $10 \div 5 = 2$
2. $12 \div 4 = 3$
3. $24 \div 6 = 4$
4. $12 \div 2 = 6$
5. $20 \div 5 = 4$
6. $9 \div 3 = 3$
7. $15 \div 5 = 3$
8. $21 \div 7 = 3$

Multiplications for each set:

1. $2 \times 5 = 10$
2. $3 \times 4 = 12$
3. $4 \times 6 = 24$
4. $6 \times 2 = 12$
5. $4 \times 5 = 20$
6. $3 \times 3 = 9$
7. $3 \times 5 = 15$

Textbook 3

8. $3 \times 7 = 21$

9.

10.

11.

12.

13.

14.

15. 11 days (2 stickers on the last day)

page 66
Dividing with remainders

1. $11 \div 3 = 3r2$
2. $17 \div 2 = 8r1$
3. $24 \div 5 = 4r4$
4. $31 \div 4 = 7r3$
5. $19 \div 3 = 6r1$
6. $34 \div 6 = 5r4$
7. $9 \div 2 = 4r1$
8. $18 \div 5 = 3r3$
9. $22 \div 4 = 5r2$
10. $40 \div 6 = 6r4$
11. $52 \div 5 = 10r2$
12. $34 \div 3 = 11r1$
Owl None
13. 5 omelettes, 1 egg left over
14. 3 coins (she bought 8 sweets).

15. Answers will vary.
16. Answers will vary.

page 67
Dividing with remainders

1. $32 \div 3 = 10r2$
2. $32 \div 4 = 8r0$
3. $32 \div 5 = 6r2$
4. $32 \div 6 = 5r2$
5. $32 \div 7 = 4r4$
6. $32 \div 8 = 4r0$
7. $32 \div 9 = 3r5$
8. $32 \div 10 = 3r2$
9. $32 \div 11 = 2r10$
Owl 9, or any other multiple of 4, plus 1 extra
10. Answers will vary. An example might be $17 \div 5 = 3r2$.

page 68
Dividing with remainders

1. $28 \div 3 = 9r1$
2. $45 \div 7 = 6r3$
3. $39 \div 4 = 9r3$
4. $27 \div 5 = 5r2$
5. $19 \div 2 = 8r3$
6. $43 \div 8 = 5r3$
7. $29 \div 9 = 3r2$
8. $19 \div 6 = 3r1$
9. $73 \div 10 = 7r3$
10. True
11. False
12. True
13. False
14. True
15. False
Owl
10. An odd number cannot be divided exactly.
11. There are exceptions, such as $88 \div 11 = 8$.
12. Multiples of 6 are divided exactly by 3, for example, $42 \div 3 = 14$.

page 68 continued

13. Odd multiples of 3, such as 21, cannot be divided exactly by 6.
14. All multiples of 10 are also multiples of 5.
15. $23 \div 4 = 5\,r\,3$, whereas $29 \div 5 = 5\,r\,4$.

page 69
Multiplying by 10 and 100

1. $3 \times 100 = 300$
2. $5 \times 100 = 500$
3. $4 \times 100 = 400$
4. $8 \times 100 = 800$
5. $6 \times 100 = 600$
6. $7 \times 100 = 700$
7. $8 \times 10 = 80\,cm$
8. $3 \times 10 = 30\,cm$
9. $6 \times 10 = 60\,cm$
10. $11 \times 10 = 110\,cm$
11. 120 seconds = 2 minutes, $2 \times 10 = 20\,cm$
12. 300 seconds = 5 minutes, $5 \times 10 = 50\,cm$
Owl 1 hour = 60 minutes, $60 \times 10 = 600\,cm$
13. $4 \times 100 = 400$
14. $7 \times 10 = 70$
15. $9 \times 100 = 900$
16. $6 \times 10 = 60$
17. $1 \times 100 = 100$
18. $2 \times 10 = 20$

page 70
Multiplying

1. $3 \times 100 = 300\,cm$
2. $7 \times 100 = 700\,cm$
3. $5 \times 100 = 500\,cm$
4. $9 \times 100 = 900\,cm$
5. $4 \cdot 5 \times 100 = 450\,cm$
6. $3 \cdot 21 \times 100 = 321\,cm$
Owl
1. $7\,m$
2. $3\,m$

3. $5\,m$
4. $1\,m$
5. $5 \cdot 5\,m$
6. $6 \cdot 79\,m$
7. $3 \times 20 = 60$
8. $4 \times 40 = 160$
9. $5 \times 30 = 150$
10. $4 \times 50 = 200$
11. $6 \times 30 = 180$
12. $3 \times 40 = 120$
Owl 6 necklaces
Beads not used = $100 + 90 + 140 + 120 + 60 = 510$

page 71
Multiplying

1. $3 \times 20p = 60p$
2. $2 \times 30p = 60p$
3. $5 \times 40p = 200p$ or £2·00
4. $7 \times 50p = 350p$ or £3·50
5. $6 \times 20p = 120p$ or £1·20
6. $4 \times 30p = 120p$ or £1·20
7. $3 \times 40p = 120p$ or £1·20
8. $9 \times 50p = 450p$ or £4·50
9. $10 \times 40p + 4 \times 50p = 600p$ or £6·00
10. $6 \times 30p + 5 \times 20p = 280p$ or £2·80
Owl 25 clown masks, 12 alien masks, 16 bear masks, 10 monkey masks
11. $3 \times 30 = 90$
12. $5 \times 40 = 200$
13. $6 \times 30 = 180$
14. $8 \times 50 = 400$
15. $40 \times 3 = 120$
16. $4 \times 20 = 80$
17. $50 \times 5 = 250$
18. $9 \times 30 = 270$
19. $2 \times 60 = 120$

page 72
Multiplying

1. 50p
2. 250 matches, 4 packs
3. 20 people

Textbook 3

4. 390 cm

5. $3 \times 40 = 120$

6. $5 \times 40 = 200$

7. $4 \times 30 = 120$

8. $60 \times 3 = 180$

9. $50 \times 3 = 150$

10. $60 \times 4 = 240$

11. $80 \times 5 = 400$

12. $7 \times 500 = 3500$

13. $9 \times 400 = 3600$

Owl $40 \times 30 = 30 \times 40$

$20 \times 50 = 50 \times 20$

page 73
Fractions

1. $\frac{1}{4}$

2. $\frac{2}{4}$

3. 0

4. $\frac{3}{4}$

5. $\frac{1}{4}$

6. $\frac{3}{4}$

7. $\frac{4}{4}$

8. $\frac{2}{4}$

Owl Answers will vary.

9. $\frac{3}{8}$

10. $\frac{5}{8}$

11. $\frac{3}{8}$

12. $\frac{5}{8}$

13. $\frac{3}{8}$

14. $\frac{5}{8}$

15. $\frac{2}{8}$

16. $\frac{2}{8}$

page 74
Fractions

1. $\frac{1}{2}$ and $\frac{2}{4}$

2. $\frac{1}{3}$ and $\frac{2}{6}$

3. $\frac{4}{6}$ and $\frac{2}{3}$

4. $\frac{3}{4}$ and $\frac{6}{8}$

5. $\frac{3}{5}$ and $\frac{6}{10}$

6. $\frac{8}{10}$ and $\frac{4}{5}$

7. $\frac{1}{4}$ and $\frac{2}{8}$

8. (a) $\frac{1}{4}$ (b) $\frac{3}{4}$

9. (c) $\frac{1}{6}$ (d) $\frac{4}{6}$ (e) $\frac{5}{6}$

10. (f) $\frac{1}{8}$ (g) $\frac{3}{8}$ (h) $\frac{5}{8}$ (i) $\frac{7}{8}$

Owl Answers will vary.

page 75
Fractions

1. $\frac{1}{2} = \frac{2}{4}$

2. $\frac{1}{3} = \frac{2}{6}$

3. $\frac{2}{3} = \frac{4}{6}$

4. $\frac{6}{6} = \frac{3}{3}$

5. $\frac{1}{2} = \frac{3}{6}$

6. $\frac{3}{4} = \frac{9}{12}$

7. $\frac{3}{12} = \frac{1}{4}$

8. $\frac{4}{12} = \frac{1}{3}$

9. $\frac{8}{12} = \frac{2}{3}$

10. True

11. Yes

page 76
Fractions

1. a & j

b & g & l & o

c & m

d & n

e & k

f & p

h & i

2. The 17 matching fractions are as follows: $\frac{1}{2} = \frac{3}{6}$, $\frac{1}{2} = \frac{4}{8}$, $\frac{1}{2} = \frac{5}{10}$, $\frac{1}{3} = \frac{2}{6}$, $\frac{1}{3} = \frac{3}{9}$, $\frac{2}{3} = \frac{4}{6}$, $\frac{2}{3} = \frac{6}{9}$, $\frac{1}{4} = \frac{2}{8}$, $\frac{2}{4} = \frac{1}{2}$, $\frac{3}{4} = \frac{6}{8}$, $\frac{1}{5} = \frac{2}{10}$, $\frac{2}{5} = \frac{4}{10}$, $\frac{3}{5} = \frac{6}{10}$, $\frac{4}{5} = \frac{8}{10}$, $\frac{2}{6} = \frac{3}{9}$, $\frac{3}{6} = \frac{4}{8}$, $\frac{4}{8} = \frac{5}{10}$

Textbook 3

page 77
Using £ and pence notation

1. £1·24
2. £3·16
3. £4·05
4. £1·55
5. £2·21
6. £6·15
7. 3 × £1, 4 × 10p, 2 × 1p
8. 5 × £1, 6 × 10p, 1× 1p
9. 2 × £1, 2 × 10p, 1× 1p
10. 3 × £1, 9 × 10p, 9 × 1p
11. 9 × £1, 3 × 10p
12. 4 × £1, 6 × 10p, 8 × 1p
13. 2 × £1, 1 × 10p, 9 × 1p
14. 1 × £1, 5 × 1p
15. False
16. True
17. False
Owl Answers will vary. Possible answers include £1·01, £1·20, £2·05, £2·50.

page 78
Using £ and pence notation

1. £4·65
2. £1·84
3. £2·57
4. £8·80
5. £1·04
6. £7·77
7. £3·56
8. £6·05
9. £9·00
10. £10·10
11. 416 days
12. 372 days
13. 281 days
14. 525 days
15. 318 days
16. 909 days
17. 1078 days
18. 660 days

Owl 13 and 15 take less than a year. 11, 12, 14, and 18 take less than 2 years.
19. £16·84
20. £1·25
Owl 8 coins: 3 × 50p, 2 × 20p, 1 × 5p, 2 × 2p

page 79
Money problems

Answers will vary.
85p: 1 × 50p, 1 × 20p, 1 × 10p, 1 × 5p
9p: 1 × 20p, 1 × 10p, 1 × 5p, 2 × 2p
13p: 1 × 10p, 1 × 2p, 1 × 1p
54p: 1 × 50p, 2 × 2p
76p: 1 × 50p, 1 × 20p, 1 × 5p, 1 × 1p
62p: 1 × 50p, 1 × 10p, 1 × 2p
95p: 1 × 50p, 2 × 20p, 1 × 5p
44p: 2 × 20p, 2 × 2p
28p: 1 × 20p, 1 × 5p, 1 × 2p, 1 × 1p
67p: 1 × 50p, 1 × 10p, 1 × 5p, 1 × 2p
The most is £2·00, the least is 20p.

page 80
Money problems

1. 1 × £2, 2 × 20p, 1 × 5p, 1 × 1p
2. 1 × £1, 1 × 10p, 1 × 5p, 2 × 2p
3. 1 × £1, 1 × 50p, 1 × 20p, 1 × 10p, 1 × 5p, 1 × 1p
4. 1 × £2, 1 × 50p, 1 × 5p, 2 × 2p
5. 1 × £2, 1 × £1, 1 × 10p, 1 × 1p
6. 2 × £2, 1 × £1, 1 × 50p, 1 × 2p, 1 × 1p
7. 2 × £2, 2 × 20p, 1 × 5p
8. 1 × £2, 1 × £1, 1 × 20p, 1 × 10p, 1 × 2p, 1 × 1p
9. 2 × £2, 1 × £1, 1 × 5p, 2 × 2p
10. 1 × £1, 1 × 50p, 2× 20p
To make the next pound:
1. £2·46 + 54p = £3
2. £1·19 + 81p = £2
3. £1·86 + 14p = £2
4. £2·59 + 41p = £3

5. £3·11 + 89p = £4
6. £5·53 + 47p = £6
7. £4·25 + 75p = £5
8. £3·33 + 67p = £4
9. £5·09 + 91p = £6
10. £1·90 + 10p = £2
11. £3·88

12. £2·53
13. £4·24, £4·34, £4·44, £4·54, £4·64, £4·74, £4·84, £4·94
14. Answers will vary. An example might be £6·31.
Owl 50p, £1, £2·50, £5, £10, £50 or £100

Block AI

PCM I
Counting in 1s

The track should be completed with the following numbers: 691, 692, 693, 694, 696, 697, 698, 699, 700, 701, 702, 703, 706, 707, 708, 709, 710, 711, 714, 715, 716, 717, 718, 719, 720, 724, 725 and 726.

PCM 2
Hundreds, tens and units

1. 243
2. 256
3. 133
4. 222
5. 183
6. 360
7. 109
8. 404
9. 160
10. 111
11. 346

PCM 3
Coins

1. Answer provided.
2. 4 × £1, 6 × 10p, 9 × 1p
3. 2 × £1, 6 × 10p, 1 × 1p
4. 3 × £1, 4 × 10p, 7 × 1p
5. 1 × £1, 4 × 10p, 6 × 1p
6. 4 × £1, 3 × 10p, 1× 1p
7. 1 × £1, 0 × 10p, 2 × 1p
8. 5 × £1, 5 × 10p, 5 × 1p

PCM 4
3-digit numbers

Answers will vary.

PCM 5
Bees

Estimate: Answers will vary.
Count: 48 bees

PCM 6
I more, I less, 100 more, 100 less

1. Answer provided.
2. 145, 146, 147
3. 758, 759, 760
4. 799, 800, 801
5. 324, 325, 326
6. 163, 164, 165
7. 998, 999, 1000
8. 143, 243, 343
9. 86, 186, 286
10. 802, 902, 1002
11. 774, 874, 974
12. 661, 761, 861
13. 455, 555, 655
14. 338, 438, 538

PCM 7
100 more, 100 less

327 → 427
416 → 516
158 → 58
273 → 373
495 → 395
627 → 527
235 → 335
348 → 248
100 more: 292, 376, 455, 719, 834, 528
100 less: 92, 176, 255, 519, 634, 328

PCM 8
1 more, 10 more

7	48
144	130
179	156
157	117
120	248
141	105
244	482
330	204
417	375
210	218

Block B1

PCM 9
Adding to 100

1. Answer provided.
2. $40 + 60 = 100$
3. $50 + 50 = 100$
4. $20 + 80 = 100$
5. $60 + 40 = 100$
6. $90 + 10 = 100$
7. $70 + 30 = 100$
8. $80 + 20 = 100$

PCM 10
Adding to 20

1. Answer provided.
2. 7
3. 10
4. 8
5. 5
6. 4
7. 9
8. 1
9. 2
10. 6
11. 0

PCM 11
Pairs to 20

1. $20 - 13 = 7$
2. $20 - 4 = 16$
3. $20 - 1 = 19$
4. $20 - 8 = 12$
5. $20 - 17 = 3$
6. $20 - 2 = 18$
7. $20 - 10 = 10$
8. $20 - 7 = 13$
9. $20 - 9 = 11$
10. $20 - 19 = 1$
11. $20 - 15 = 5$
12. $20 - 6 = 14$
13. $20 - 2 = 18$
14. $20 - 14 = 6$

PCM 12
Adding three numbers

1. Answer provided.
2. $4 + 6 + 7 = 17$
3. $4 + 8 + 6 = 18$
4. $7 + 3 + 3 = 13$
5. $2 + 8 + 9 = 19$
6. $8 + 6 + 2 = 16$
7. $7 + 8 + 3 = 18$
8. $10 + 9 + 0 = 19$
9. $1 + 7 + 9 = 17$
10. $9 + 3 + 1 = 13$
11. $1 + 1 + 9 = 11$
12. $7 + 5 + 3 = 15$
13. $4 + 4 + 6 = 14$
14. $8 + 2 + 2 = 12$
15. $9 + 2 + 1 = 12$
16. $5 + 4 + 5 = 14$
17. $6 + 6 + 4 = 16$
18. $2 + 8 + 1 = 11$
19. $4 + 5 + 6 = 15$
20. $5 + 6 + 5 = 16$

PCM 13

Shapes

Patterns should be continued and shaded appropriately, as below.

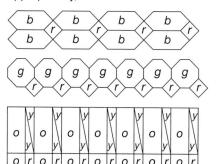

r=red *o*=orange *y*=yellow
b=blue *g*=green

Patterns will vary.

PCM 14

Names of shapes

1. Answer provided.
2. Triangle
3. Octagon
4. Pentagon
5. Square
6. Hexagon
7. Triangle
8. Pentagon
9. Hexagon

Answers will vary.

PCM 15

Symmetry

1.

2.

3.

4.

5.

6.

PCM 16

Symmetry

1. Answer provided.

2.

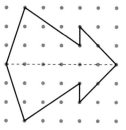

3.

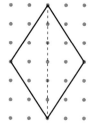

4.

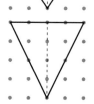

Photocopy Masters

5.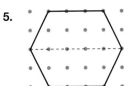

6.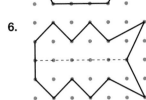

7.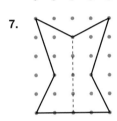

Answers will vary.

Block CI

PCM I7
Metres

1. 1 m
2. 2 m
3–8. Answers will vary.

PCM I8
Centimetres

Answers will vary.

PCM I9
Metres and centimetres

1. 135 cm
2. 210 cm
3. 300 cm
4. 150 cm
5. 250 cm
6. 458 cm
7. 607 cm
8. 2000 cm
9. 2·45 m
10. 3·25 m
11. 4·0 m
12. 1·5 m
13. 2·08 m
14. 3·06 m
15. 0·65 m
16. 3·5 m

PCM 20
Tally chart

Transport	Tallies	Total
skateboard	|||||	5
bicycle	||||| ||||	9
tricycle	||||| ||	7
scooter	|||||		6
roller blades	||||	4

1. 31
2. Bicycle
3. Roller blades

PCM 2I
Pictograph

1. green
2. blue
3. red
4. yellow
5. green
6. blue
7. red
8. blue
9. blue
10. green
11. 24

Block DI

PCM 22
Adding

1. $16 + 4 = 20$
2. $24 + 6 = 30$
3. $13 + 5 = 18$
4. $16 + 3 = 19$
5. $20 + 4 = 24$
6. $23 + 5 = 28$
7. $24 + 4 = 28$
8. $23 + 3 = 26$
9. $31 + 5 = 36$
10. $40 + 1 = 41$
11. $20 + 9 = 29$
12. $22 + 5 = 27$
13. $23 + 2 = 25$
14. $31 + 7 = 38$
15. $27 + 7 = 34$
16. $14 + 7 = 21$
17. $26 + 9 = 35$
18. $18 + 5 = 23$
19. $31 + 9 = 40$
20. $33 + 4 = 37$
21. $26 + 6 = 32$
22. $15 + 7 = 22$
23. $33 + 6 = 39$
24. $23 + 8 = 31$
25. $25 + 5 = 30$
26. $21 + 6 = 27$
27. $31 + 8 = 39$
28. $24 + 9 = 33$
29. $11 + 7 = 18$
30. $13 + 4 = 17$

PCM 23
Problems

1. 17p
2. 39p
3. 19p
4. 4 sweets
5. 18 years
6. 25 years
7. 11:47
8. 12

PCM 24
Subtracting

1. $25 - 5 = 20$
2. $36 - 6 = 30$
3. $18 - 8 = 10$
4. $47 - 7 = 40$
5. $29 - 9 = 20$
6. $54 - 4 = 50$
7. $26 - 6 = 20$
8. $38 - 8 = 30$
9. $19 - 9 = 10$
10. $42 - 2 = 40$
11. $55 - 5 = 50$
12. $34 - 4 = 30$
13. $32 - 2 = 30$
14. $75 - 5 = 70$
15. $57 - 7 = 50$
16. $24 - 4 = 20$
17. $43 - 3 = 40$
18. $98 - 8 = 90$

PCM 25
Subtracting

1. $18 - 6 = 12$
2. $15 - 5 = 10$
3. $22 - 4 = 18$
4. $13 - 4 = 9$
5. $23 - 8 = 15$
6. $24 - 5 = 19$
7. $17 - 3 = 14$
8. $35 - 8 = 27$
9. $31 - 7 = 24$
10. $21 - 8 = 13$
11. $33 - 4 = 29$
12. $15 - 7 = 8$
13. $24 - 8 = 16$
14. $26 - 9 = 17$
15. $15 - 6 = 9$
16. $34 - 4 = 30$
17. $30 - 8 = 22$
18. $33 - 8 = 25$

19. 32 − 9 = 23
20. 26 − 6 = 20

PCM 26
Problems

1. 21 points
2. 32 children
3. 12p
4. 7p
5. 19p
6. 30 years
7. 47p
8. 29p
9. 24 cm
10. 11 miles

PCM 27
Minutes

1. 20 minutes
2. 10 minutes
3. 15 minutes
4. 45 minutes
5. 25 minutes
6. 40 minutes
7. 55 minutes
8. 35 minutes

PCM 28
Five minutes

1. 8:00
2. 8:05
3. 8:10
4. 8:15
5. 8:20
6. 8:25
7. 8:30
8. 8:35
9. 8:40
10. 8:45
11. 8:50
12. 8:55

Block EI

PCM 29
Multiplying and dividing

1. Answer provided.
2. $4 \times 4 = 16$
$16 \div 4 = 4$
3. $2 \times 8 = 16$
$16 \div 8 = 2$
4. $4 \times 7 = 28$
$28 \div 7 = 4$
5. $5 \times 3 = 15$
$15 \div 3 = 5$
6. $3 \times 7 = 21$
$21 \div 7 = 3$
7. $3 \times 5 = 15$
$15 \div 5 = 3$

PCM 30
Multiplying and dividing

1. $3 \times 5 = 15$
$15 \div 5 = 3$
2. $4 \times 3 = 12$
$12 \div 3 = 4$
3. $2 \times 4 = 8$
$8 \div 4 = 2$
4. $5 \times 4 = 20$
$20 \div 4 = 5$
5. $6 \times 4 = 24$
$24 \div 4 = 6$
6. $7 \times 3 = 21$
$21 \div 3 = 7$
7. $8 \times 2 = 16$
$16 \div 2 = 8$
8. $1 \times 3 = 3$
$3 \div 3 = 1$
9. $6 \times 10 = 60$
$60 \div 10 = 6$
10. $9 \times 2 = 18$
$18 \div 2 = 9$

PCM 31

Twos

1. $4 \times 2 = 8$
2. $8 \times 2 = 16$
3. $9 \times 2 = 18$
4. $10 \times 2 = 20$
5. $2 \times 2 = 4$
6. $5 \times 2 = 10$
7. $3 \times 2 = 6$
8. $1 \times 2 = 2$
9. $6 \times 2 = 12$
10. $7 \times 2 = 14$
11. $11 \times 2 = 22$
12. $12 \times 2 = 24$
13. $50 \times 2 = 100$

PCM 32

Dividing by 2

1. $12 \div 2 = 6$
2. $8 \div 2 = 4$
3. $2 \div 2 = 1$
4. $10 \div 2 = 5$
5. $14 \div 2 = 7$
6. $4 \div 2 = 2$
7. $20 \div 2 = 10$
8. $16 \div 2 = 8$
9. $6 \div 2 = 3$
10. $18 \div 2 = 9$
11. $100 \div 2 = 50$
12. $40 \div 2 = 20$
13. $50 \div 2 = 25$
14. $1000 \div 2 = 500$

PCM 33

Fractions

1. Answer provided.
2. $\frac{1}{4}$ of $8 = 2$
3. $\frac{1}{2}$ of $6 = 3$
4. $\frac{1}{3}$ of $12 = 4$
5. $\frac{1}{3}$ of $6 = 2$
6. $\frac{1}{2}$ of $12 = 6$
7. $\frac{1}{4}$ of $12 = 3$
8. $\frac{1}{2}$ of $4 = 2$
9. $\frac{1}{4}$ of $16 = 4$

PCM 34

Fractions

1. Answer provided.
2. $\frac{1}{2}$ of $10p = 5p$
3. $\frac{1}{4}$ of $20p = 5p$
4. $\frac{1}{4}$ of $8p = 2p$
5. $\frac{1}{2}$ of $12p = 6p$
6. $\frac{1}{4}$ of $12p = 3p$
7. $\frac{1}{3}$ of $12p = 4p$
8. $\frac{1}{3}$ of $15p = 5p$
9. $\frac{1}{4}$ of $80p = 20p$
10. $\frac{1}{2}$ of $£1 = 50p$
11. $\frac{1}{5}$ of $£1 = 20p$
12. $\frac{1}{10}$ of $£1 = 10p$

PCM 35

Fractions

1. Answer provided.
2. Answer provided.
3. $\frac{1}{4}$ of $12 = 3$
4. $\frac{1}{2}$ of $20 = 10$
5. $\frac{1}{2}$ of $50 = 25$
6. $\frac{1}{4}$ of $24 = 6$
7. $\frac{1}{4}$ of $20 = 5$
8. $\frac{1}{3}$ of $21 = 7$
9. $\frac{1}{2}$ of $30 = 15$
10. $\frac{1}{3}$ of $27 = 9$
11. $\frac{1}{3}$ of $60 = 20$
12. $\frac{1}{4}$ of $100 = 25$
13. $\frac{1}{3}$ of $30 = 10$
14. $\frac{1}{2}$ of $14 = 7$
15. $\frac{1}{4}$ of $32 = 8$
16. $\frac{1}{2}$ of $18 = 9$

PCM 36
Doubling

1. double 2p = 4p
2. double 5p = 10p
3. double 7p = 14p
4. double 11p = 22p
5. double 12p = 24p
6. double 15p = 30p
7. double 30p = 60p
8. double 32p = 64p

PCM 37
Doubling and halving

6 and 12
8 and 16
11 and 22
13 and 26
15 and 30
21 and 42
43 and 86

PCM 38
Doubling machine

in	21	24	32	23	14	41	31	42
out	42	48	64	46	28	82	62	84

in	11	34	22	12	44	33	13	43
out	22	68	44	24	88	66	26	86

in	25	5	45	75	15	65	35	55
out	50	10	90	150	30	130	70	110

Block A2
PCM 39

Nearest 10

Aliens coloured blue: 56, 59, 61, 63, 64
Aliens coloured green: 28, 31, 32, 34
Aliens coloured orange: 6, 7, 9, 14
Aliens coloured yellow: 85, 89, 91, 92, 94

PCM 40
Between

1. 116
2. 237
3. 300
4. 401
5. 599
6. 644
7. 265
8. 110
9. 709
10. 600

PCM 41
Ordering

85, 97, 102, 111, 120
256, 348, 417, 526, 634
408, 452, 463, 471, 479
320, 329, 330, 331, 333
757, 758, 759, 760, 761

PCM 42
3-digit numbers
Answers will vary.

PCM 43
Multiples

	multiple of 10	multiple of 50	multiple of 100	multiple of 2	multiple of 5
630	✓	✗	✗	✓	✓
950	✓	✓	✗	✓	✓
35	✗	✗	✗	✗	✓
180	✓	✗	✗	✓	✓
220	✓	✗	✗	✓	✓
95	✗	✗	✗	✗	✓
20	✓	✗	✗	✓	✓
46	✗	✗	✗	✓	✗
17	✗	✗	✗	✗	✗
100	✓	✓	✓	✓	✓

PCM 44

Odd and even

b 1	r 2	b 3	r 4	b 5	r 6	b 7	r 8	b 9	r 10
b 11	r 12	b 13	r 14	b 15	r 16	b 17	r 18	b 19	r 20
b 21	r 22	b 23	r 24	b 25	r 26	b 27	r 28	b 29	r 30
b 31	r 32	b 33	r 34	b 35	r 36	b 37	r 38	b 39	r 40
b 41	r 42	b 43	r 44	b 45	r 46	b 47	r 48	b 49	r 50
b 51	r 52	b 53	r 54	b 55	r 56	b 57	r 58	b 59	r 60
b 61	r 62	b 63	r 64	b 65	r 66	b 67	r 68	b 69	r 70
b 71	r 72	b 73	r 74	b 75	r 76	b 77	r 78	b 79	r 80
b 81	r 82	b 83	r 84	b 85	r 86	b 87	r 88	b 89	r 90
b 91	r 92	b 93	r 94	b 95	r 96	b 97	r 98	b 99	r 100

r = red b = blue

Block B2

PCM 45

Missing numbers

1. $30 + 70 = 100$
2. $60 + 40 = 100$
3. $80 + 20 = 100$
4. $10 + 90 = 100$
5. $50 + 50 = 100$
6. $40 + 60 = 100$
7. $70 + 30 = 100$
8. $20 + 80 = 100$
9. $90 + 10 = 100$
10. $35 + 65 = 100$
11. $25 + 75 = 100$
12. $85 + 15 = 100$
13. $45 + 55 = 100$
14. $65 + 35 = 100$
15. $15 + 85 = 100$
16. $75 + 25 = 100$
17. $5 + 95 = 100$
18. $55 + 45 = 100$

PCM 46

Adding to 100

52	43	11	89	44	25
36	65	27	18	46	75
31	35	48	26	54	19
69	33	72	28	10	30
72	45	55	43	90	20
8	92	16	59	27	80

For the second half of the exercise, answers will vary depending on the numbers children write in their grids.

PCM 47

Adding to the next 100

1. $155 + 45 = 200$
2. $278 + 22 = 300$
3. $369 + 31 = 400$
4. $87 + 13 = 100$
5. $525 + 75 = 600$
6. $471 + 29 = 500$
7. $456 + 44 = 500$
8. $183 + 17 = 200$
9. $397 + 3 = 400$
10. $204 + 96 = 300$
11. $535 + 65 = 600$
12. $726 + 74 = 800$
13. $894 + 6 = 900$
14. $962 + 38 = 1000$

PCM 48

Adding to make 100

1. $47 + 53 = 100$
2. $32 + 68 = 100$
3. $54 + 46 = 100$
4. $83 + 17 = 100$
5. $21 + 79 = 100$
6. $56 + 44 = 100$
7. $38 + 62 = 100$
8. $79 + 21 = 100$

9. $100 - 77 = 33$ children
10. $100 - 84 = 16$ years
11. $100 - 58 = 42\,cm$

PCM 49
Shapes

Square-based pyramid

Triangular prism

Cube

Cuboid

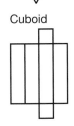

Triangle-based pyramid

Block C2
PCM 50
Litres and millilitres

1. 1200 ml
2. 2400 ml
3. 5000 ml
4. 3500 ml
5. 1700 ml
6. 4600 ml
7. 2500 ml
8. 1500 ml
9. 1 l 500 ml
10. 2 l 300 ml
11. 0 l 700 ml
12. 3 l 0 ml
13. 1 l 500 ml
14. 5 l 600 ml
15. 1 l 100 ml
16. 4 l 500 ml

PCM 51
Hours and minutes

1. 70 mins
2. 150 mins
3. 115 mins
4. 125 mins
5. 90 mins
6. 135 mins
7. 210 mins
8. 240 mins
9. 1 hr 30 mins
10. 2 hrs 10 mins
11. 1 hr 5 mins
12. 3 hrs 20 mins
13. 1 hr 40 mins
14. 0 hrs 50 mins
15. 1 hr 30 mins
16. 3 hrs 15 mins

PCM 52
Frequency table

Vowel	Tallies
a	JHT JHT JHT JHT JHT
e	JHT JHT JHT JHT I
i	JHT I
o	JHT
u	JHT I

Vowel	Frequency
a	25
e	21
i	6
o	5
u	6

1. a
2. o

Photocopy Masters

PCM 53
Bar graph

1. 24
   28
2. Wednesday
   Tuesday
   Thursday
   Friday
   Saturday
3. 2 days
   2 days
4. 164

Block D2
PCM 54
Adding multiples of 10

1. Answer provided.
2. 90
3. 80
4. 90
5. 110
6. 70 (left hand box),
   80 (right hand box)
   Total: 150
7. 70 (left hand box),
   40 (right hand box)
   Total: 110
8. 160
9. 80 (left hand box),
   90 (right hand box)
   Total: 170
10–13. Answers will vary, depending on the order in which children write the numbers on the bottom row.

PCM 55
Subtracting multiples of 10

Answers will vary.

PCM 56
Subtracting 20, 30, 50

11	5	26
9	43	14
32	7	55

9	61	26
52	18	21
34	40	43

13	39	42
22	30	25
7	34	43

PCM 57
Adding two 2-digit numbers

1. Answer provided.
2. $31 + 45 = 76$
3. $26 + 32 = 58$
4. $18 + 21 = 39$
5. $43 + 55 = 98$
6. $27 + 52 = 79$
7. $36 + 26 = 62$
8. $58 + 25 = 83$
9. $18 + 34 = 52$
10. $27 + 16 = 43$
11. $73 + 19 = 92$
12. $45 + 46 = 91$
13. $53 + 28 = 81$
14. $27 + 37 = 64$
15. $45 + 28 = 73$
16. $35 + 45 = 80$

PCM 58
Adding two 2-digit numbers

1. Answer provided.
2. $35 + 27 = 62$
3. $27 + 38 = 65$
4. $35 + 38$ or $27 + 46 = 73$

Photocopy Masters

5. 59 + 18 = 77
6. 27 + 18 = 45
7. 59 + 35 = 94
8. 18 + 38 = 56
9. 59 + 46 = 105

PCM 59
Adding multiples of 10

Answers will vary.

PCM 60
Adding 9, 19 and 29

Answers will vary.

PCM 61
Subtracting 19

1. Answer provided.
2. 54p – 19p = 35p
3. 35p – 19p = 16p
4. 26p – 19p = 7p
5. 41p – 19p = 22p
6. 70p – 19p = 51p
7. 64p – 19p = 45p
8. 87p – 19p = 68p
9. 63p – 19p = 44p
10. 51p – 19p = 32p
11. 45p – 19p = 26p
12. 22p – 19p = 3p

PCM 62
Adding and subtracting 9, 19, 29

1. 43 + 19 = 62
2. 54 + 9 = 63
3. 72 + 29 = 101
4. 81 + 19 = 100
5. 68 + 29 = 97
6. 29 + 19 = 48
7. 37 – 9 = 28
8. 46 – 19 = 27

9. 38 – 29 = 9
10. 37 – 29 = 8
11. 46 + 9 = 55
12. 55 + 19 = 74
13. 87 – 19 = 68
14. 64 – 19 = 45
15. 82 + 29 = 111
16. 75 – 29 = 46
17. 63 – 19 = 44
18. 52 – 9 = 43
19. 14 + 39 = 53
20. 42 + 39 = 81

Block E2

PCM 63
Tens

3 and 30
10 and 100
9 and 90
4 and 40
5 and 50
6 and 60
2 and 20
8 and 80
7 and 70
1 and 10

PCM 64
Fives

1. Answer provided.
2. 4 × 5 = 20
3. 6 × 5 = 30
4. 4 × 5 = 20
5. 5 × 5 = 25
6. 2 × 5 = 10
7. 2 × 5 = 10
8. 9 × 5 = 45
9. 10 × 5 = 50
10. 8 × 5 = 40

PCM 64 continued

11. $12 \times 5 = 60$
12. $8 \times 5 = 40$
13. $6 \times 5 = 30$
14. $10 \times 5 = 50$
15. $1 \times 5 = 5$

PCM 65
Dividing by 5 and 10

1. $30 \div 10 = 3$
2. $10 \div 5 = 2$
3. $25 \div 5 = 5$
4. $50 \div 5 = 10$
5. $15 \div 5 = 3$
6. $70 \div 10 = 7$
7. $35 \div 5 = 7$
8. $20 \div 5 = 4$
9. $45 \div 5 = 9$
10. $40 \div 5 = 8$
11. $100 \div 10 = 10$
12. $30 \div 5 = 6$
13. $5 \div 5 = 1$
14. $1000 \div 10 = 100$

PCM 66
Multiplying

1. Answer provided.
2. B and H $6 \times 3 = 3 \times 6$
3. C and I $3 \times 5 = 5 \times 3$
4. D and J $2 \times 3 = 3 \times 2$
5. E and G $4 \times 5 = 5 \times 4$

PCM 67
Multiplying

1. Answer provided.
2. $3 \times 4 = 12$
3. $5 \times 2 = 10$
4. $3 \times 6 = 18$
5. $5 \times 4 = 20$
6. $6 \times 4 = 24$
7. $2 \times 4 = 8$
8. $4 \times 4 = 16$

PCM 68
Threes

PCM 69
Threes

PCM 70
Counting in sixes

1. 6, 12, 18, 24, 30, 36, 42, 48, 54, 60, 66

2.

$1 \times 3 = 3$	$1 \times 6 = 6$
$2 \times 3 = 6$	$2 \times 6 = 12$
$3 \times 3 = 9$	$3 \times 6 = 18$
$4 \times 3 = 12$	$4 \times 6 = 24$
$5 \times 3 = 15$	$5 \times 6 = 30$
$6 \times 3 = 18$	$6 \times 6 = 36$
$7 \times 3 = 21$	$7 \times 6 = 42$
$8 \times 3 = 24$	$8 \times 6 = 48$
$9 \times 3 = 27$	$9 \times 6 = 54$
$10 \times 3 = 30$	$10 \times 6 = 60$

PCM 71
Dividing by 3

1. $12 \div 3 = 4$
2. $6 \div 3 = 2$

3. $15 \div 3 = 5$
4. $30 \div 3 = 10$
5. $9 \div 3 = 3$
6. $18 \div 3 = 6$
7. $21 \div 3 = 7$
8. $3 \div 3 = 1$
9. $27 \div 3 = 9$
10. $24 \div 3 = 8$
11. $60 \div 3 = 20$
12. $300 \div 3 = 100$
13. $33 \div 3 = 11$
14. $36 \div 3 = 12$

PCM 72
Fractions

PCM 73
Fractions

1. $\frac{2}{8}$ or $\frac{1}{4}$
2. $\frac{3}{8}$
3. $\frac{4}{8}$ or $\frac{1}{2}$
4. $\frac{7}{8}$
5. $\frac{3}{8}$
6. $\frac{5}{8}$
7. $\frac{2}{8}$ or $\frac{1}{4}$
8. $\frac{1}{8}$

PCM 74
Fractions

1. Answer provided.
2. $\frac{2}{3}$ of 9 = 6
3. $\frac{7}{8}$ of 24 = 21
4. $\frac{3}{5}$ of 10 = 6
5. $\frac{5}{6}$ of 18 = 15
6. $\frac{1}{4}$ of 16 = 4
7. $\frac{2}{5}$ of 15 = 6
8. $\frac{1}{8}$ of 16 = 2

Block A3

PCM 75
Nearest 100

1. Answer provided.
2–12. In any order as follows:

$247 \rightarrow 200$
$249 \rightarrow 200$
$274 \rightarrow 300$
$279 \rightarrow 300$
$297 \rightarrow 300$
$427 \rightarrow 400$
$429 \rightarrow 400$
$472 \rightarrow 500$
$479 \rightarrow 500$
$492 \rightarrow 500$
$497 \rightarrow 500$
$724 \rightarrow 700$
$729 \rightarrow 700$
$742 \rightarrow 700$
$749 \rightarrow 700$
$792 \rightarrow 800$
$794 \rightarrow 800$
$924 \rightarrow 900$
$927 \rightarrow 900$
$942 \rightarrow 900$
$947 \rightarrow 900$
$972 \rightarrow 1000$
$974 \rightarrow 1000$

PCM 76
Nearest 10

1. Answer provided.
2. 8 from: 475, 476, 477, 478, 479, 481, 482, 483, 484
3. 8 from: 325, 326, 327, 328, 329, 331, 332, 333, 334
4. 8 from: 205, 206, 207, 208, 209, 211, 212, 213, 214
5. 8 from: 795, 796, 797, 798, 799, 801, 802, 803, 804
6. 8 from: 945, 946, 947, 948, 949, 951, 952, 953, 954
7. 8 from: 685, 686, 687, 688, 689, 691, 692, 693, 694

PCM 77
Rounding 3-digit numbers to nearest 10

1. £130
2. £360
3. £720
4. £700
5. £280
6. £490
7. £150
8. £400
9. £830
10. £470
11. £190
12. £510
13. £245, £246, £247, £248, £249, £251, £252, £253, £254
14. £635, £636, £637, £638, £639, £641, £642, £643, £644
15. £695, £696, £697, £698, £699, £701, £702, £703, £704
16. £1225, £1226, £1227, £1228, £1229, £1231, £1232, £1233, £1234
17. Answers will vary

PCM 78
Buying

Answer provided.
£3·52: £3·21, £3·28, £3·35
£1·94: £1·63, £1·70, £1·77
£4·53: £4·22, £4·29, £4·36
£3·27: £2·96, £3·03, £3·10
£2·71: £2·40, £2·47, £2·54

PCM 79
Subtracting money

£1·75: £1·55, £1·25, £1·45
£2·45: £2·25, £1·95, £2·15
£2·99: £2·79, £2·49, £2·69
£1·79: £1·59, £1·29, £1·49
£4·25: £4·05, £3·75, £3·95
£3·15: £2·95, £2·65, £2·85
£4·75: £4·55, £4·25, £4·45
99p: 79p, 49p, 69p

PCM 80
Adding money

1. £1·95
2. 60p
3. £1·60
4. £2·85
5. £1·95
6. 70p
7. £2·85
8. £1·70
9. £1·85
10. £1·70

PCM 81
Problems

1. £2·85
2. £1·65
3. £3·55
4. £4·15
5. £6·90
6. £3·40

7. 25p
8. £5·70
9. £5·40
10. £5·65

PCM 82
Adding

1. 124 + 13 = 137
2. 361 + 17 = 378
3. 237 + 21 = 258
4. 172 + 16 = 188
5. 464 + 31 = 495
6. 423 + 23 = 446
7. 313 + 73 = 386
8. 315 + 51 = 366
9. 506 + 63 = 569
10. 384 + 13 = 397
11. 632 + 47 = 679
12. 621 + 78 = 699
13. 444 + 45 = 489
14. 364 + 21 = 385
15. 225 + 54 = 279
16. 576 + 21 = 597

PCM 83
Problems

1. 168
2. 229
3. 219 days
4. 116
5. 325 points
6. 53p
7. 147
8. 75p

PCM 84
Adding near doubles

1. 23 + 24 = 47
2. 24 + 25 = 49
3. 45 + 47 = 92
4. 12 + 13 = 25
5. 16 + 17 = 33
6. 32 + 33 = 65

7. 31 + 32 = 63
8. 47 + 48 = 95
9. 17 + 19 = 36
10. 26 + 27 = 53
11. 44 + 45 = 89
12. 45 + 46 = 91
13. 11 + 13 = 24
14. 21 + 23 = 44
15. 38 + 39 = 77
16. 41 + 42 = 83
17. 34 + 36 = 70
18. 27 + 29 = 56

PCM 85
Next-door numbers

6 + 7 = 13
19 + 20 = 39
31 + 32 = 63
3 + 4 = 7
15 + 16 = 31
1 + 2 = 3
23 + 24 = 47
29 + 30 = 59
9 + 10 = 19
39 + 40 = 79
12 + 13 = 25
33 + 34 = 67
21 + 22 = 43
17 + 18 = 35
25 + 26 = 51

Block B3

PCM 86
Even and odd

1. 16 + 5 = 21 (green)
2. 8 + 8 = 16 (yellow)
3. 6 + 7 = 13 (green)
4. 17 + 9 = 26 (yellow)
5. 12 + 2 = 14 (yellow)
6. 11 + 6 = 17 (green)
7. 12 + 3 = 15 (green)
8. 15 + 5 = 20 (yellow)
9. 16 + 2 = 18 (yellow)

PCM 86 continued

10. $17 + 8 = 25$ (green)
11. $21 + 3 = 24$ (yellow)
12. $16 + 3 = 19$ (green)
13. $17 + 5 = 22$ (yellow)
14. $21 + 2 = 23$ (green)

PCM 87

Fours

16	8	24
12	32	4
28	20	36

8	36	16
32	20	40
24	12	28

24	40	12
16	32	28
36	44	20

PCM 88

Threes and fours

No answers required.

PCM 89

Fours

1. $4 \times 2 = 8$
2. $4 \times 4 = 16$
3. $10 \times 2 = 20$
4. $10 \times 4 = 40$
5. $3 \times 2 = 6$
6. $3 \times 4 = 12$
7. $5 \times 2 = 10$
8. $5 \times 4 = 20$
9. $7 \times 2 = 14$
10. $7 \times 4 = 28$
11. $9 \times 2 = 18$
12. $9 \times 4 = 36$
13. $8 \times 2 = 16$
14. $8 \times 4 = 32$
15. $11 \times 2 = 22$
16. $11 \times 4 = 44$

PCM 90

Right angles

The angles will be coloured:
1. yellow
2. green
3. blue
4. green
5. yellow
6. yellow
7. yellow
8. blue
9. yellow

PCM 91

Right angles

Right angles: A, D, G, H, I, L

PCM 92

North, South, East and West

1. Answer provided.
2. S
3. S
4. E
5. S
6. E
7. N
8. W
9. N
10. W
11. N
12. W

PCM 93

North, South, East and West

No answers required.

PCM 94

North, South, East and West

1. Answer provided.
2. East 4, North 2, East 2, South 6
3. North 4, West 4, South 5, East 6, North 3
4. East 2, North 4, East 2, South 2, East 2, North 4

5. West 3, North 2, West 1, South 4, East 6, North 3

Block C3

PCM 95
Grams

1–9. Answers will vary.

PCM 96
Grams and kilograms

1. Answer provided.
2. 500 g
3. 50 g
4. 600 kg
5. 1 kg

Totals	1 kg	500 g	200 g	100 g	50 g	20 g
650 g		✓		✓	✓	
270 g			✓		✓	✓
850 g		✓	✓	✓	✓	
1520 g	✓	✓				✓
1870 g	✓	✓	✓	✓	✓	✓

PCM 97
Position

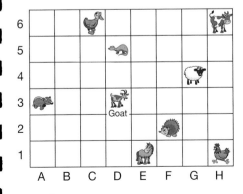

9. Otter
10. Cow
11. Badger

PCM 98
Days and weeks

10 days
1 week and 3 days
8 days
1 week and 1 day
22 days
3 weeks and 1 day
15 days
2 weeks and 1 day

PCM 99
Venn diagrams

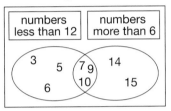

PCM 100
Venn diagrams

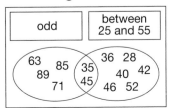

a double	digit total more than 7

Left circle only: 40 42 52
Intersection: 28 36 46
Right circle only: 35 45 71 63 89 85

PCM 101
Carroll diagrams

1. $2 + 4 = 6$
2. $16 - 3 = 13$
3. $6 + 9 = 15$
4. $5 + 6 = 11$
5. $20 - 8 = 12$
6. $10 - 2 = 8$
7. $23 - 6 = 17$
8. $10 + 10 = 20$
9. $13 - 9 = 4$
10. $3 + 2 + 2 = 7$
11. $8 + 8 = 16$
12. $4 + 3 + 2 = 9$

	less than 14	not less than 14
even	4 6 8 12	16 20
odd	7 9 11 13	15 17

Block D3
PCM 102
Adding hundreds, tens and units

Answers will vary.

PCM 103
Adding hundreds, tens and units

1. $303 + 325 = 628$
2. $435 + 604 = 1039$
3. $104 + 507 = 611$
4. $125 + 236 = 361$
5. $212 + 158 = 370$

6. $119 + 203 = 322$
7. $321 + 216 = 537$
8. $205 + 192 = 397$
9. $433 + 247 = 680$
10. $174 + 322 = 496$
11. $346 + 243 = 589$
12. $152 + 427 = 579$

PCM 104
Adding using formal methods

Answers will vary.

PCM 105
Adding using formal methods

1. Answer provided.
2. 684
3. 801
4. 702
5. 692
6. 705
7. 697
8. 802
9. 784
10. 798
11. 809
12. 808

PCM 106
Adding using formal methods

Answers will vary.

PCM 107
Difference

d	21	26	19	24
14	7	12	5	10
19	2	7	0	5
27	6	1	8	3
22	1	4	3	2

Photocopy Masters

d	30	35	27	23
25	5	10	2	2
31	1	4	4	8
29	1	6	2	6
38	8	3	11	15

d	47	41	43	32
37	10	4	6	5
49	2	8	6	17
39	8	2	4	7
40	7	1	3	8

d	66	59	62	54
58	8	1	4	4
61	5	2	1	7
53	13	6	9	1
67	1	8	5	13

PCM 108
Problems

1. 6 years
2. 8
3. 7p
4. 121 cm
5. 19
6. 22
7. £14
8. 13

PCM 109
Subtracting 3-digit numbers

1. $254 - 110 = 144$
2. $456 - 220 = 236$
3. $383 - 150 = 233$
4. $248 - 140 = 108$
5. $469 - 220 = 249$
6. $339 - 130 = 209$
7. $657 - 230 = 427$
8. $731 - 170 = 561$
9. $752 - 520 = 232$
10. $626 - 310 = 316$
11. $157 - 90 = 67$
12. $364 - 170 = 194$
13. $532 - 430 = 102$
14. $753 - 270 = 483$

Block E3
PCM 110
Dividing

1. Answer provided.
2. $8 \div 4 = 2$
3. $12 \div 4 = 3$
4. $9 \div 3 = 3$
5. $6 \div 2 = 3$
6. $12 \div 3 = 4$
7. $18 \div 9 = 2$
8. $27 \div 9 = 3$
9. $21 \div 7 = 3$

PCM 111
Dividing with remainders

1. $9 \div 4 = 2 \, r1$
2. $7 \div 2 = 3 \, r1$
3. $4 \div 3 = 1 \, r1$
4. $11 \div 4 = 2 \, r3$
5. $11 \div 3 = 3 \, r2$
6. $19 \div 2 = 9 \, r1$
7. $17 \div 5 = 3 \, r2$
8. $47 \div 10 = 4 \, r7$
9. $8 \div 3 = 2 \, r2$
10. $17 \div 4 = 4 \, r1$
11. $13 \div 2 = 6 \, r1$
12. $38 \div 5 = 7 \, r3$
13. $33 \div 10 = 3 \, r3$
14. $26 \div 4 = 6 \, r2$
15. $17 \div 3 = 5 \, r2$
16. $46 \div 5 = 9 \, r1$

PCM 112
Multiplying by 10 and 100

1. $9 \times 10 = 90$
2. $7 \times 10 = 70$
3. $3 \times 10 = 30$
4. $18 \times 10 = 180$
5. $16 \times 10 = 160$
6. $12 \times 10 = 120$
7. $24 \times 100 = 2400$
8. $36 \times 100 = 3600$
9. $91 \times 100 = 9100$
10. $56 \times 10 = 560$
11. $80 \times 10 = 800$
12. $26 \times 10 = 260$
13. $160 \times 10 = 1600$
14. $8 \times 100 = 800$
15. $31 \times 100 = 3100$
16. $240 \times 10 = 2400$
17. $150 \times 10 = 1500$
18. $38 \times 100 = 3800$

PCM 113
Multiplying

1. $4 \times 30 = 120$
2. $3 \times 40 = 120$
3. $3 \times 20 = 60$
4. $5 \times 20 = 100$
5. $2 \times 40 = 80$
6. $4 \times 40 = 160$
7. $5 \times 30 = 150$
8. $6 \times 30 = 180$
9. $7 \times 30 = 210$
10. $8 \times 30 = 240$
11. $3 \times 50 = 150$
12. $4 \times 60 = 240$
13. $5 \times 40 = 200$
14. $7 \times 20 = 140$
15. $9 \times 30 = 270$
16. $7 \times 40 = 280$
17. $8 \times 40 = 320$
18. $4 \times 70 = 280$
19. $3 \times 60 = 180$
20. $6 \times 60 = 360$

PCM 114
Multiplying

Answers will vary.

PCM 115
Fractions

1. Answer provided.
2. $\frac{1}{3}$ $\frac{2}{6}$
3. $\frac{3}{4}$ $\frac{6}{8}$
4. $\frac{2}{3}$ $\frac{4}{6}$
5. $\frac{1}{4}$ $\frac{2}{8}$
6. $\frac{1}{2}$ $\frac{4}{8}$
7. $\frac{2}{5}$ $\frac{4}{10}$

PCM 116
Fractions

1. $\frac{1}{3} = \frac{2}{6}$
2. $\frac{3}{6} = \frac{2}{4}$
3. $\frac{2}{3} = \frac{4}{6}$
4. $\frac{3}{6} = \frac{6}{12}$
5. $\frac{9}{12} = \frac{3}{4}$
6. $\frac{1}{2} = \frac{2}{4}$
7. $\frac{3}{6} = \frac{1}{2}$
8. $\frac{5}{6} = \frac{10}{12}$
9. $\frac{3}{12} = \frac{1}{4}$
10. $\frac{1}{3} = \frac{4}{12}$
11. $\frac{1}{2} = \frac{6}{12}$
12. $1 = \frac{6}{6}$

PCM 117
Money problems

1. 60p
2. 20p
3. 30p
4. 55p

5. 36p
6. 43p
7. 85p
8. 42p

PCM 118
Money problems

58p
32p
13p
16p
60p
25p
17p

PCM 119
Money problems

1. Answer provided.
2. 10p, 5p, 1p
3. 20p, 10p, 5p
4. 20p, 20p, 2p
5. 10p, 5p, 2p, 2p
6. 20p, 5p, 2p
7. 50p, 2p, 1p
8. 50p, 10p, 5p, 2p
9. 50p, 20p, 5p, 2p, 1p
10. 50p, 20p, 10p, 1p
11. 20p, 10p, 5p, 2p, 1p
12. 20p, 20p, 5p, 2p, 2p

PCM 120
Money problems

	£2	£1	50p	20p	10p	5p	2p	1p	Total coins
68p			1		1	1	1	1	5
95p			1	2		1			4
£1·21		1		1				1	3
£2·40	1			2					3
£1·64		1	1		1		2		5
85p			1	1	1	1			4
£1·07		1				1	1		3
£3·60	1	1	1		1				4
£3·17	1	1			1	1	1		5